Soul Care
A Guided Prayer Journal and Planner
for Women

Letting go of Emotional, Mental, and Spiritual Exhaustion
for a Rested, Renewed, Abundant Life

Alisha C. Walker, LPC

ISBN 978-1-7363198-0-2

ABOUT THE AUTHOR

Alisha Curry Walker has a passion to help others live the life they desire and deserve. She's been on a path to help others succeed for over 20 years. She does this as a Licensed Professional Counselor, Certified Professional Counselor Supervisor, Board Certified – Telemental Health Provider, Speaker, Author and Coach. She has counseled thousands of people, dealing with issues that range in diversity from anxiety and trauma, to parenting and marital / relationship issues. She has forged a path on several roads to infuse her passion for mental health and wellness, resilience and self-care, which she calls soul care. She has a desire to hold the hope for the hopeless, provide encouragement to the lost, shine a light on what success means to you and lead the parade for all those that will listen about the benefits of mental health and wellness and resilience.

She is a graduate of Florida A&M University with a BS in Psychology and Nova Southeastern University with an MS in Mental Health Counseling. In her career, in addition to counseling, she has spoken to audiences as small as 4 or 5 to an audiences of thousands. She speaks with confidence, authority and conviction and always brings practical tips that her audience can implement right away. She is compassionate and supportive but knows how to hold clients and audiences alike accountable for the information that she shares.

Alisha has published numerous articles on self-care, mental health and wellness, spiritual wellness and marriage and relationships. She's even written a book for couples, _I Love Being Married: A Guide to Divorceproof Your Marriage_ .

She has has been married for 21 years and has 5 beautiful children. As a family they have endured some soul shaking events, which have fueled her passions even further to help motivate and inspire others to live the life they desire and deserve.

For more information or to contact Alisha, please go to www.soulcarebooks.com

ACKNOWLEDGEMENTS

I thank God for giving me the vision for the book and commitment to see it through.

I am so grateful for the love and undying support of my husband, Benjamin Walker, Jr.

I am thankful for my children, Brandon, Alexis, Allana, Aaliyah and Angelique. The desire to want to be a better woman comes from my desire to be the best example of a godly woman for them. I appreciate their love, support and even their accountability.

I am thankful for my parents, Thomas and Gwendolyn Curry for always loving and supporting me. I am grateful that I continue to feel their love and support daily.

"If you don't design your own life plan, chances are you'll fall into someone else's plan. And guess what they have planned for you? Not much."

JIM ROHN

This Journal Belongs to:

_____

The Setup

CHAPTER 1

Going Beyond Self-Care

*I*NTRODUCTION

I am so happy that you picked up Soul Care. This is a guided prayer journal and planner. My overall goal in writing this book is to help you let go of emotional, physical and spiritual exhaustion, fear feelings of being stuck and live the abundant life that God intends for you to live. My prayer is that this journal is a blessing to you and will give you peace. I pray that in these pages you will find the identity of who God says that you are and that you will fight fiercely to align yourself with her and live the life that God has ordained for you to live. In John 10:10, NASB the bible says, The thief comes only to steal and kill and destroy; I came that they may have life, and have it abundantly. This book is meant for you to do the work to finally live the abundant life that God has called for you to live. The methods I use in this book are the same that I use in my Soul Care Coaching for myself and the women I work with.

This guide and the work that I do is to help you overcome those things that are stealing and destroying your mental health, your relationships, your marriage, your parenting, your success. Many people try to put a bandaid on those things and cover them up, run away from them or not acknowledge them at all, or fight against anything that comes to help, but doing these things is causing depression, anxiety, overwhelm and exhaustion. This guide is meant to help you identify the gaps between who you are now and how you live and your true identity of who God created you to be.

Are you feeling anxious about where you are in your life now? Do you feel like you need more direction to truly live an abundant life? Do you feel like you are truly living in the identity and the calling that God has for you? Do you feel like something is missing in your life, but you are stuck on how to truly make lasting changes? Where do you see yourself? What would your life look like if you were living the life you know God has designed for you? What do you believe is getting in your way? If you could get rid of the things that are getting in your way, keeping you stuck, mentally, emotionally, spiritually exhausted, what could your life look like? What would be possible?

I want to help you make that life you just imagined possible. The one you believe that God is calling you to. The one that you feel led to live through the process in this book.

My prayer is that throughout these pages, you will do the work through what I call soul care, so that your identity will line up with God's vision for you and when it does, you will be able to let go and release the emotional, physical and spiritual exhaustion and find rest, renewal and replenishment in God and who he says that you are. You will be able to exhale. Your yoke will be easy and your burdens will be light because you would have aligned yourself with God's call on your life. Even those hard areas will become lighter with Him.

What is Soul Care and Why is it Important to you?

Soul care is you partnering with God to begin to shape and mold you into the woman that God has called to be. It is creating a relationship with him based on trust, faith and friendship - a knowing that He loves you and always wants the best for you.

Using the term soul care in this way allows you to dig deeper into the issues, patterns of behaviors, way of thinking, choices that you've made that have kept you stuck. Soul care allows you to pinpoint the area or areas in your life that cause a nagging sense of anxiety, discontent or restlessness because you are not fully living the life that God has called for you to live and making you tired. Being misaligned or off in any of these areas at your core will cause you to feel like you need to do something to take care of yourself like your soul needs to be taken care of because deep down you know you are "misliving" . (A term coined by William Irvine) When living with a daily life in true soul care you are living in abundance.

Soul care is the total picture of who you are and all of the areas that are a part of your makeup. I call it soul care because a big part of it is based on your identity in God and who you believe yourself to be in Him. Your trust and belief in who he says that you are in spite of all of what your life may have shaped up to be or what you believe it looks like now.

Inspiration for this Journal - My Story

I want this journal to be a life changer for you. In fact that is my prayer for you. I am doing this because I was pushed, nudged, confronted by God. Let me explain. I had been plugging along with my life which was pretty normal by all accounts with the usual ups and downs. But then about 9 years ago we had a child that was born with Sickle Cell and our lives were turned upside down all of what we were used to and how we operated was completely changed.

My daughter, Angelique was hospitalized more than 12 times with 3 of them being surgeries, all before the age of 2. Devastated was an understatement. My whole world stopped so that I could take care of her. Then when she turned 2 we started asking about a Bone Marrow Transplant (BMT) as a cure for her Sickle Cell. She received the BMT when she was 4 and was cured and is now the healthiest one in the family at 10 years old.

Tired in every sense of the word, depleted, overloaded, overwhelmed

After this, I promised myself and God that I would live life to the fullest and I started doing that. I also said over and over I just want a normal life like everyone else where we could just go to church, go to school not have to worry about hospitalizations, just be normal have the regular hustle and bustle like everyone else.

So after her year of recovery I went back to work. I worked for a non-profit providing training on many things, but one of the topics that stuck out to me was trauma. Even in the midst of everything that went on during my daughter's Sickle Cell and Transplant journey, I didn't realize that I had been traumatized by all that we had gone through and was still reeling from. I just wanted to be quiet. I was on empty and really couldn't pour out to anyone else, I was emotionally and spiritually exhausted.

My career prior to my daughter's bone marrow journey was as a therapist serving and working with couples and families. During this time, I was beginning to feel depleted because I was giving so much out to others. So, I started seeing fewer and fewer clients because I just couldn't fully give myself to the work and felt it wasn't fair to them. Even after the ordeal with my daughter, I was gun shy. I settled into an aspect of my journey as a therapist that didn't require me to fully show up to give of myself in that way.

Fast forward 2 years and I left that job and got back into working for myself providing counseling and continuing to do trainings. I was doing the work that I thought I should be doing. I was rebuilding my business. In the midst of this I joined a business group that promoted helping you build your business and I had some success but not the amount that I felt I could have. It really had nothing to do with them, it had everything to do with me. I really didn't realize how much building a business pushes on who you are as a persona and your own personal growth and development.

I didn't realize that your business can't grow any further than your beliefs. So in the business I had doubts about myself, my work, compared to others in the group who seemed to be shining. It was like all of my insecurities were being highlighted. A few months into the group, my second oldest daughter was diagnosed with a rare autoimmune disease that came out of NOWHERE. When I say no where we had no clue that this was on the horizon. This took me OUT. I was stuck in Lord why and why her why me why us, I really am just getting over the other one and finding a groove again. Eventually I sort of pull myself out of it but still feeling like I'm floundering trying to find my way out of this and not really seeing the right direction.

I go back to what I know works and begin to be silent, seek God, wise counsel, pray, read my bible, talk it through, journal, listen to books, podcasts, read, spend time with my family, circle my wagons as I call it. All of these things were working but I still felt like I was moving in slow motion.

Then one day after a church service after weeks of me feeling like God was talking to me through sermons, books, podcasts all of the things i was reading was pointing me in a similar direction, but I felt stuck I wasn't moving and it all came to a head. One of the ministers at my church was leaving and moving away. My pastor said if you want to say goodbye before she leaves wait after service to speak to her, there may be a line, but wait to speak to her, so I did.

There was a line, my family was waiting for me and in fact I had said my goodbyes to her two weeks earlier when they announced that she was leaving. But I couldn't leave, I walked out a few times headed to the car with my family, but I couldn't leave, I went back in. And what I know now is that it was God pushing me. So I went back in and waited to talk to her. She was talking to other people, but I waited.

When I got up to her, she grabbed my hand, gave me a hug and looked me dead in my eye and said "stop hiding". Wait! What did she just say? Did she just say what I think she said? All kinds of thoughts started running through my head. I felt so vulnerable at that moment. It was like she was looking right through me and knew exactly what was going on even if I didn't believe I was hiding. So as she is talking, I tried to pull away, my eyes started to fill up and I quietly said "don't do that". She grabbed my hand even harder and wouldn't let me go. I thought, Lord , why is this woman saying this to me? Matthew 18:12-14 NKJV (God will seek out the 1 from the 100)

Mind you I didn't really know her. We talked briefly maybe once or twice. I was in a small group that she was leading at church and I spoke out in that group a few times but not a lot. When we were actually in church service, we would greet each other, smile and give a hug, but that was it. We had never really talked in-depth. She didn't know me. We hadn't spent that much time together. So anyway, as I'm trying to pull away, she grabs my hand squeezes it and says it again, stop hiding, you have so much to offer . Couples need you, women need you, people need you, it's time for you to stand up. I tried to pull away again and I said don't do that, then she squeezed my hand again. Of course at this point I'm crying and she's continuing to hold my hand and is looking not just into my eyes, but into my soul and said stop hiding, stand up. When I tell you that I was too through at this point, I was. I was done. I was shook. Shaken to my core because I knew in my heart of hearts that she was right that I had been hiding, that God had so much more for me and for me to do and I wasn't doing it. I wasn't living up to who and what he has for me. I wasn't joining him or going with his flow, I was creating my own and running from what he wanted for me. So after she finished she let my hand go, gave me a hug and said keep in touch, you have my information. Call me.

God gave me the idea for this book two years ago. I started on the journey, then let it go to pursue what I thought was going to bring the most financial gain at the time, but it never felt right. I was pushing, pulling, trying to make things happen instead of truly aligning my gifts, skills and talents with who I am and with who God has called me to be and in doing so I wasn't happy. I was misaligned. My soul was anxious because it couldn't rest and no amount of self care activities were helping me to quiet the anxiety in my soul.

God will come find you even when you don't want to be found, when he knows that he has more for you but you are living below what he has for you. Below where he has called you to be below where you know you need to be. This is why the usual things like spending time with friends, going to get massages or manicures, don't fill you up because they are not a real replacement for the life that you know you should be living and are not.

Are you ready for more? Then keep reading.Allow this book to become that moment for you, where God hems you up, where He comes after you and finds you.

He has not forgotten you. He has not forgotten the promises He made you. He has not forgotten the prayers you've prayed even the ones you haven't prayed because deep down you're too afraid to pray.

He has not forgotten even those things that you've given up praying for that thing that seems ever present and is just a part of your life and you have said to yourself, it is what it is. He has not forgotten you.

What You Can Expect from this Journal

This book was created to help you design your life the way God intended you to live. He gave us life that we might have life more abundantly. To live our lives according to how He sees us at His level and not below. Nothing short of abundance. If anyone understands, I do that life is full of ups and downs and some things that come can be completely unexpected, but all of these life "experiences" come to help shape us into the person, God wants you to be. These experiences can also steal your joy, push you down, have you feel like God can't use you in this state. John 10:10 (NASB) says "The thief comes only to steal and kill and destroy; I came that they may have life and have it abundantly". "And we know that all things work together for good to those who love God, to those who are called according to His purpose" Romans 8:28, NKJV

Yes life has a way of pulling, pushing and making you feel pressed on all sides, but God will always make a way. I know that when you're in the middle of this you may be tired, weary and are just looking for a path forward other than being stuck. (Like the Israelites needing to cross the red sea.)

This book is a guide to help you discover the life that God has truly meant for you to have. To discover your distinct makeup and how what you've been through, how you're wired and who you are aligns so that you can walk out the life that God has called you to live. The purpose and the call on your life.

You'll begin to understand that soul care is a lifestyle and not a last ditch effort. You'll learn to implement soul care daily to fuel your soul. When you've finished the book you will have a daily soul care routine that refuels you to prevent getting to a place of an empty cup. You will achieve a daily routine of soul care that meets your need for the moment and not random actions that don't help. You will find the things that really feed your soul that will keep you in alignment with your abundant life.

What your brain may be telling you. You will be pushed in areas that you have left alone or run away from because you're just not that good at that or you're comfortable where you are or you kind of just looked up one day and you didn't recognize yourself or your life. I know some things have come to mind as you read this.

You can expect that your status quo will be challenged, you will be pushed to think of new ways to live the life that you say you want and to use this new way of living to truly live and walk in your purpose and live on a level that not only matches the dreams that you have for yourself but the plans that God has for you. It's ok to be in tears after reading this statement. If you put in the work, it will be true for you.

There are three sections in the book to help you get to the end where you can practically walk out this plan for your life on a daily basis.

1. Section one will help you understand the definition of soul care, God's plan for abundance and why you need to go beyond self care to move into a life of peace, joy and abundance.
2. Section two will help discover the gaps between your identity and God's identity for you and how this gap is causing you stress, exhaustion, fear and overwhelm.
3. Section three will help you choose the top priority area that you'll work on 1st that will give you the most bang for your buck and could possibly impact the other areas you want to focus on.

How to use this Journal

If you are tired, anxious or maybe even exhausted with the hustle and bustle of life and need a way to just breathe, this book is for you. If you feel like you've been pushing and pulling in too many areas in your life and you want to find that rest, that joy, that peace that you see others have, then this book is for you.

This book is a mashup of sorts. It is part guided journal, part prayer journal and part goal planner. I thoroughly believe that the best way to incorporate what you learn is to implement it into your life. In the guided and prayer journal sections there will be prompts for you to read and respond to and even write prayers for. In the planner section, the task is for you to create a plan to implement what you've learned and discovered in the journal sections. In the answered prayers (gratitude journal) section of the book, you are to write the prayers that you see that God has answered along the way. It is an account, a way to be grateful for the journey and a tool to use as a reminder when the enemy tries to steal, kill and destroy.

It is your answer to his tactics to keep a yoke of fear, anxiety, stress and negative thinking over your life and a way to remind you of God's truths not just from the bible, but from the way he has walked it out in your life personally.

The book is designed in this way to help you

1. Reveal the issues that have been getting in your way of truly living the abundant life that God has created for you.
2. Discover what your abundant life is meant to look like in every area learn
3. Develop a plan to become this woman through daily, intentional action, put it into action so that you can create the daily habits of the person that you will discover in these pages. The person God has called you to be.
4. Become the woman God has called for you to be and live a rested, renewed, abundant life

My Prayer for You

My prayer for you is that you discover whatever has been holding you back, causing you pain, making you feel tired, overwhelmed, stressed, angry, anxious, unsettled or even exhausted and that you are set free. My prayer for you is that in these pages, you will find rest, peace and renewal in the place that God is calling you to and that you step up and rise to that place that He is calling you to so that you can have life and have it more abundantly.

Make the commitment to do the work.

Your pledge – your commitment

You know how people take a before picture for weight loss. I want you to take a before picture and paste it here. Take a picture of yourself today as you start this journey and describe what you see. Commit to God that you will do the work this time to become the woman he has called you to be in ALL areas of your life. Commit that you will fight through the desire to fall back into old habits and behaviors that no longer serve you. Commit to loving God and allowing him to love and take care of you. Commit to trusting God and allowing him to shape your belief about yourself so that it aligns with who he says that you are. Commit to doing the work to become the woman that you've dreamed of.

Write Your Commitment Here:

Prayer

Thank God for the opportunity for you to let go of your mental, emotional and spiritual exhaustion and the ability to find peace, renewal, abundance and purpose. Ask God to show you what He'd like for you to gain from doing the work in this book. Ask God to give you the strength to be diligent in doing the work and to listen for his voice and direction as you move through the book. Write your prayer here and what you hope to gain from this book. Write a specific prayer of where you want to see God take you when you've finished this book. It can be something you've prayed before, something that you've been too afraid to pray or something that has been too painful. It can be that thing that you've prayed for but have just gotten comfortable with it being a part of your life, but deep down you know it doesn't have to be a part of your life.

Post your picture and your prayer below:

CHAPTER 2

God's Plan for Abundance

God's Plan for Abundance

God's plan for abundance in your life is to have your life align with the vision, the dream that he has for you. His plan is to love you no matter the circumstance and for you to feel that love whatever you're going through. In turn, because you are so loved by him, you'll be able to give to others from your overflow. A place of abundance and not lack. Living an abundant life is living a blessed life. A life where you feel taken care of, even in those areas where by all accounts you shouldn't. God's plan for abundance is for you to have a peace that surpasses all understanding because you are going with His flow and reliant on him for everything. You are following the path that God has laid for you because you trust that he wants the best for you even in those times that are uncomfortable or painful. In order to have this type of abundance, there has to be a relationship with God and just like the cornerstone of any relationship, you have to trust God.

Faith, Trust, and Obedience

How much do you trust God? Do you trust God in every area of your life?Before starting the journey to write this book I would have said I trust God. And in certain areas of my life I really did, but in others, it is now evident that I didn't. The areas of my life where I felt I was either not living up to my potential or those areas that seemed like there was a struggle or like I was fighting. Areas where I felt like I was pushing and pulling or areas where I felt like things were a struggle. I felt there was no grace in those areas. Even in those areas, God cares for you. Even in those areas, He wants you to feel his love and there was a time where I felt or thought that I trusted God in all that I do, but I realized that there were certain areas that I was taking back the control from God that I wasn't in partnership with him and that I was moving ahead of him and that I was taking the reins. God wants to be in partnership with you over your life. He wants to be in relationship with you. He will never force you, never push you, never make you. He wants you to be in relationship with him. He is done so he is kind. he goes above and beyond and he wants you to do well. He wants to support you. He wants you to be your best and all that you do.

Think about it, if you have children and you have a plan for their life or you have an idea of where you want their life to be headed, you do your best to ensure that they have the best possible life you bend over backwards to ensure that if you could get it for them or you could do it for them or you could help support them through it that you do that. That's how God feels about you. He wants to support you. He wants to love you. He wants you to feel like no matter what he will bend over backwards to ensure that your life is full of love, full of grace and full of abundance.

The areas of my life that I knew I gave control over to God were my family, my children and my marriage. There was even a point where I felt like God was truly looking out for those areas in my life, but I personally felt that something was missing. I felt like I was missing the mark and that things that I personally wanted weren't happening weren't coming into fruition. I felt like God was honoring, blessing and moving into abundance everything and everyone around me but not me personally. However, when I really sat down and listened and had a conversation with God, I realized that I didn't fully trust him. I wasn't being obedient to what he had told me to do and in doing so I cut off my opportunity for abundance. I cut off my opportunity to be blessed. I got ahead of or got in the way of God wanting to bless me. I stopped just short of what God told me to do and did things my way. It was as if as soon as I got close to the more, the abundance was calling me to personally, I sabotaged it, got in the way and did things in my own strength. I took it back from God after I left it at His feet, because I didn't fully trust that He would take care of me.

Is there an area(s) in your life that came to mind that you now realize that you don't fully trust God? If so, write them here.

Is there something or someone standing in the way of you trusting God? Write that here:

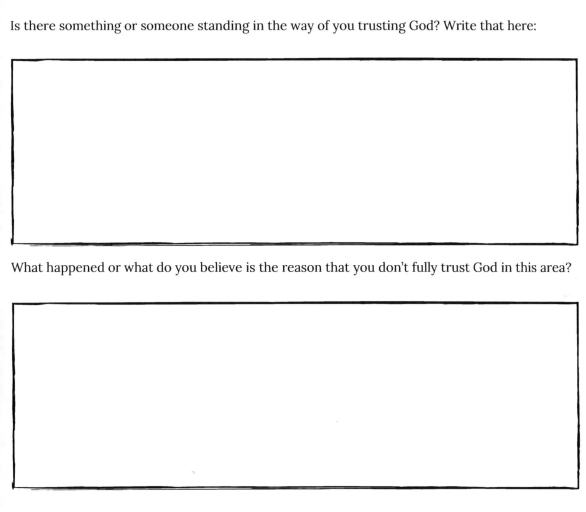

What happened or what do you believe is the reason that you don't fully trust God in this area?

What I realized is I had a strong relationship with God and was aligned with His vision for my life in certain areas. The areas of my life that I felt there was an abundance of love, overflow, grace and peace. The areas where I didn't feel and abundance of love, overflow, grace and peace were the areas that I was continuing to try to control. So the areas where I trusted God, it was easy for me to be obedient to His will. I had evidence to support and back up the claim in my head that he could be trusted. I had faith in those areas that God would come through no matter what. I believed that God loved me enough to take care of me in those areas. But what about the other areas where there was a lack of trust, faith and obedience? In Chapter 8, we will do a deep dive into how to rebuild your trust in God and grow your faith to believe what He says about you and to move closer to the woman God has called you to be.

You are a Friend of God

John 5:15 (Abide in me) To have life more abundantly, you have to take an active role. You are a participant and you are a partner in shaping what living life abundantly to the full looks like in every area of your life. To create this partnership, this friendship, you have to spend time with God so that you can trust him and know his voice and his plan for your life. Spending time with God creates the climate for abundance. God wants your life to be a reflection of Him and his plan for your life. The only way to know his plan for your life is to spend time with Him.

How much time do you spend with God?

How do you spend time with God?

How would you describe your friendship with God?

How do you speak to God?

How does God speak to you?

When you think about the people in your life that you consider a good friend or even a best friend, what are the qualities that you think of? Write them here:

Would you describe your relationship with God in the same way? Why or why not?

In order to become friends with this person, what are the things that you did to get to know them?

How did you learn to trust them?

God wants a relationship with us that is marked by us spending so much time with him that we can recognize his voice and when he is speaking to us. He can use whatever means he sees fit to speak to you. The ways that God can use to speak to you and that you can spend time with him are:

- Reading your bible
- Praying
- Meditating on the bible
- Meditating on the words God has spoken to you
- Being in quiet reflection
- Journaling
- Sermons
- Books, music, podcasts on the messages of God
- Reading Devotions
- Taking Bible study classes or being in small groups
- Talking to God

Which of these do you do? Or write your own.

How often do you incorporate them into your daily life?

Which do you think you could do more of to improve your relationship with God?

Seasons of Life / Pruning

The final section on abundance calls for a conversation on seasons of life and pruning. In Ecclesiastes 3, the bible talks about how there a season for everything under the sun. A time to weep and a time to laugh, a time to mourn and a time to rejoice. These verses are saying that in everyone's life there are seasons of ups and downs. One has to occur to be able to appreciate the other. And in having these seasons, it can feel at times that God is distant or that we don't fully feel his love. This is why relationship is so important. Have you ever dated someone and there was a time in the relationship where you felt distant or disconnected from them? When you look back on that time, was one of the main reasons you felt distant because you weren't spending enough time together? Or not spending enough meaningful time together?

Now there are seasons of life where there are droughts. There are seasons of life where you have to go through a season of quiet and a season of connecting more with God to hear what he has to say to you. Then there are seasons of your life where you are being pruned and shaped to go to the next level of grace and abundance that God has for you, going from fruit to more fruit. When God is pruning you, it can feel very uncomfortable. He is shaping and cutting away those people, places and things that don't line up with His vision for you. He is also shaping, pruning and cutting away those old thought patterns that minimize your worth, make you feel less than and that align with your abundant life. It's important that you recognize what those seasons look like so that you are not fighting against the work that God is doing in you. The only way that you can recognize the pruning that is going on in your life is to spend time with God. By spending time with him, he will reveal to you through all of the areas mentioned above ie: prayer, journaling what areas that he is pruning in you. You will begin to recognize themes of things that God wants to shape in you because there will be a sermon, a bible verse, a devotion or someone personally talking to you and you will feel a nudge like they are talking to you. It will begin to appear over and over and you will begin to recognize how this area is out of alignment with God's vision for you. Then he will begin to work on you to shape and mold that area to look more like that vision. It becomes harder when you fight against what God is doing.

Ask God to reveal to you the areas of your life that don't align with Him and that he is pruning?
Write them here:

Commitment:

Answer the questions in this chapter.

Read Ephesians 2-3

Spend some time with God to cultivate your relationship by:

1. Reading your bible
2. Prayer
3. Journaling
4. Listening to or watching sermons
5. Or something else that you choose

Write your commitment here:

Prayer:

Thank God for his commitment to you and his love for you. Ask God to help appreciate his love and begin to trust him with all areas of your life. Thank God for the opportunity to co-create and abundant life with him.

Write your prayer about abundance below:

CHAPTER 3

How Your Identity is Formed

How Identity is formed
Why what you believe Dictates where you will go

We each have our own journey and how we've gotten to this place in our lives. We've had highs, lows, good times and bad, but all of them are a part of your story and all of them make up who we are. Each moment in your life has helped to shape your soul - mind, will and emotions. Each moment has helped shape how you see the world, how you see yourself and how you see God. What if there was a way to change this? What if you could make intentional changes to begin to partner with God to shape your life into a shared vision he has for you?

Let's talk about how you got to this point. You have an identity that has been formed over time by, guess what - your mind, will and emotions. Your identity is the totality of you. Your identity is your thoughts and emotions connecting to form a belief that then informs how you will behave. Over time, because our brains aren't designed to hold millions of thoughts at once, it creates a continued thought, emotion, behavior combination. Then that combination becomes encased into a habit. That belief and series of habits then creates the identity. You've been creating the identity that you have for however many years you've been alive. You can have the identity of victim, conqueror, someone with strength, someone who folds under pressure, someone who doesn't stand up for themselves, someone who settles for less, someone who walks in their purpose, someone who lives an abundant life. How you identify yourself is up to you, but the way God identifies you is up to him. The disconnect comes when the way you identify yourself doesn't line up with the way God sees you and this is why you have that nagging gnawing feeling that there must be more; the reason you feel burdened to do more even if other people around you see that you already have so much.

What's God's Plan for Your Identity, Ephesians 2:10

Ephesians 2:10 For we are his workmanship [His own master work, a work of art], created in Christ Jesus [reborn from above - spiritually, transformed, renewed, ready to be used] for good works, which God prepared [for us] beforehand [taking paths which He set], so that we would walk in them [living the good life which He prearranged and made ready for us].

God's plan for your identity is to use every part of you in partnership with Him. His plan for you is to incorporate every part of how he has made you and what he's called for you to be. In Jeremiah 29:11, God knew you before you were born into this world he knew what you would have to offer and his plan for your identity is related to who he knew you would be. The problem arises when we fight against who God has called us to be or we try to put ourselves into different compartments and only show part of ourselves to those around us depending on the situation. We do this because we are hiding that area, don't think we're good enough or we doubt or are afraid in this area. God's call for your identity is for you to be completely fully and wholly you, no matter what situation that you're in. God has a plan for each of our lives and for every piece of our lives to come into an alignment of who he's called for us to be and it is our job to live out in that sweet spot and in that sweet spot, we will live in abundance.

God's plan for you is to be authentically who you are. Be in alignment with what you believe, who you are what you know yourself to be, who He knows you to be. When your thoughts, behaviors, habits, feelings and your identity are out of alignment, you act out of character and live a life that is not worthy of who you are. and other people can treat you how they see fit versus how you see is best for you. When moving in alignment you are more at peace, you let go of the things that other people have put on you and you walk more in your purpose, your values, who you say you are. Knowing who you are can cut down on the stress, anxiety and all those things that don't line up with who you know yourself to be. All of those things that are out of character for you, all of those things that bring a burden to you. You can easily recognize them when you are in alignment and you are aware of who you are. You become less tolerant of other people wasting your time, your energy, your money. A lot of people become aware of this later in life or some people lose sight of it because of life and other circumstances that clouds it for them but getting into true alignment of who you are helps you walk in that alignment and live a more happy and abundant life.

God wants to use all of you. God wants your gifts to be a part of his kingdom to help others but it is also a part of his promise that you will live an abundant life and living abundantly means that you are living in alignment with yourself, with him and you are able to use all of your gifts, you are not compartmentalizing, you are not putting things into different compartments that don't line up.

When you are out of alignment, things are uncomfortable and uneasy, you're not sure of yourself and it is a lot easier for other people to put certain commands or demands on you because you're not certain of your time, your energy or your efforts.

Here's an example, if you believe that you are skilled at cooking then you consider yourself a good cook and probably those around you consider you a good cook as well. But if every time you go to cook something you burn it or it doesn't quite meet the taste test that you have your belief could be that you're not a good cook.

Somewhere in there you've acquired either the identity of a good cook or a bad cook and your thoughts emotions beliefs behaviors and habits support your identity of a good or a bad cook in order to change your identity from a bad cook to a good cook you have to change your thoughts your feelings or behaviors your beliefs and your habits around cooking. Imagine a good cook that you know of in your family what are some of the things that they do? Do they enjoy cooking? Do you and other people enjoy their food? Do you and other people believe that they are good cook? does this person believe that there are good cook? When they cook do they read recipes do they create their own recipes do they watch cooking videos? People who believe that they are good cooks display the habit behaviors thoughts beliefs and emotions of a good cook. In this chapter, we are going to discover the identity of where you see yourself and the identity of where God sees you.

What are some of the ways that you identify yourself? A good wife, a great parent, a savvy businesswoman? A bad friend, a victim, a people pleaser? The way we identify ourselves can either serve us well or take away from us. We just have to decide which ways we identify ourselves serve us well and continue those and work to remove the ways that don't.

Write down how you identify yourself below:

God sees us as his unique masterpiece. Each of us is made differently and uniquely. All of what we've been through helps to shape this identity, which is a part of what makes us unique. None of us have the same experience even if we grew up in the same home. Because God has had a plan for you and a vision for you before you were born, he has gifted you with unique gifts and abilities.

Our lives are then shaped in a way that allows us to choose to use those gifts in alignment with God's dream for us or one of our own design. Think about your gifts like the parable of the talents in Matthew 25:14. Three different servants were given talents and two of the three sowed their talents or invested their talents. The third servant buried his talent out of fear. The two that sowed their talents were rewarded and were blessed with more. The one who hid his talent had his talent taken away and he was in a place of lack. God did not give you your gifts and abilities to hide, he gave them to you to share with others, to sow into others so that he can bless you and you then in turn will be a blessing to others through your overflow. We have to be good stewards of the gift God has given us, good stewards over our identity, God's calling on our life.

Are there any areas in your life that you've hidden or buried because you thought God couldn't use them? If so, write them here.

Our identity is impacted by how we see ourselves and our circumstances. Our brain plays a huge role in how we live our lives. The brain is made up of different sections that controls certain aspects of what we do. Because most of what we think 80-90% comes from our subconscious brain, the life that we live now is a reflection of those thoughts. This happens because our brain creates neural pathways based on what we think. So for example if you think, I'm not good enough over and over again, eventually, you don't have to consciously think it anymore.

www.soulcarebooks.com

So anytime there is something that is outside of your comfort zone, your brain will go to the default of "I'm not good enough". This will keep happening even though you don't want it to. There may even be something that you've wanted to do for a long time and you keep stopping and you never understood why. This is why. You have subconsciously told yourself over and over again that you are not good enough so now it has become an automatic thought and comes up anytime something is hard or it's something you may desire that is different from what you're used to. So overtime the thoughts you think the things you tell yourself begin to form pathways in your mind that you don't even realize that they are there. Just as much as the negative can create a pathway, so can the positive. The problem is the negative automatic thoughts are the ones that get in the way, keep you stuck or make you feel like you have one foot on the pedal and one foot on the gas of your life and you feel like you are not moving.

What are some areas in your life that you feel like you are at a standstill or feel stuck?

What are some thoughts that you have been telling yourself and didn't realize it? Write them below. (Ie: I'm not good enough. You can't trust people, they always hurt you. If I try, they will find out that I don't know what I'm doing.)

What is the number one lie that you have been telling yourself that has been holding you back?

YOUR AUTOMATIC NEGATIVE THOUGHTS

Day	Time	Event	Automatic Negative Thoughts

Directions:

Keep a log of your automatic thoughts over the next 7 days.

Complete this log for at least 7 days so that you can recognize any patterns that emerge.

Where's Your Focus

One of the reasons why what you believe dictates where you will go is based on where you put your focus. Have you ever noticed that if you decide you want to buy a new car, dress, pair of shoes, you start seeing others of the same type? Or have you noticed that when you're in the beginning stage of a diet, it seems like everything you see has to do with foods, particularly the foods that are your weakness? Or have you noticed?

This is due to a part of the brain called the Reticular Activating System (RAS). The RAS simply put means what you focus on grows, What you focus on or pay attention to will continue to come in your view because you have seen it as a focus. When it comes to your identity, what you focus on grows. So if you doubt yourself, feel like you're not good enough, don't feel like you measure up, you will notice those areas more that support that thought process because that's your focus. On the other hand if you see yourself as courageous, capable, happy, fulfilled, living on purpose, you will notice these areas more because that's your focus. Changing, pruning, or creating new neural pathways is possible to create the focus, life and lifestyle that aligns with God's plan for abundance for your life. That aligns with his identity for you.

And how you see these things. The filter or the lens that you see these things through. You can either see them through any negative automatic thoughts or you can see them through a positive filter. The positive filter is joy, gratitude, love and appreciation. These filters allows you to create a new neural pathway even with old thinking that allows you to see the possibilities, recognize a positive future.

It becomes hard to put on this positive filter because we are acting out of 80-90% of our subconscious brain. So when you are trying to do something new with all the right motives and then you just get stuck it's because this new thing doesn't line up with how you truly think and feel about yourself. It doesn't fully compute and it causes what's called cognitive dissonance also known as stress or anxiety because the new you that you see doesn't line up with your subconscious belief about yourself.

The good news is that God says in Romans 12:2 that we can renew our minds and science says the same through a concept called neuroplasticity.

Neuroplasticity basically says that our brains are not fixed at any moment in time and what you believe today can be changed and shaped into something else. A true change takes about 67 days, not the 21 days that everyone quotes as the amount of time that it takes to change a habit. In these 67 days, if you are deliberate, intentional and mindful about changing, you can do so and filter in what God says about you and your life.

Just as you have formed patterns of thoughts, emotions and behaviors that have formed your current identity, it is possible to create and forge your new identity based on how Christ sees you by intentionally forming new neural pathways that align with who God has called you to be.

In the next chapter we'll talk about how we will do this and break down the steps we'll take to get you there..

Commitment:

Answer the questions in this chapter.
1. Read Ephesians 2:10
2. Complete the questions and tables in this chapter.
3. Become mindful of your automatic negative thoughts

Write your commitment here:

Prayer:

Ask God to show you how he sees you and his plan for your life. Ask God to help shape your identity so that it aligns with his will for your life. Pray for clarity and focus on the areas of your life that he is shaping and pruning and ask for guidance on how to walk in this season of your life.

Write your prayer about identity below:

The Process

CHAPTER 4

Renew Your Mind

RENEW YOUR MIND

The first three chapters were the set up helping you understand what God's plan for a rested, renewed and abundant life looks like. This next section of chapters in the process are designed to be particularly personal to you, your relationship with yourself, others and God. In this section we will do a deep dive into what's really shaped you up to this point in your life no matter how old you are so that you can then create your own personalized plan to walk in the life that God has planned for you. Are you ready?

This section hinges on Romans 12:2. (MSG)

And do not be conformed to this world [any longer with its superficial values and customs], but be transformed and progressively changed [as you mature spiritually] by the renewing of your mind [focusing on godly values and ethical attitudes], so that you may prove [for yourselves] what the will of God is, that which is good and acceptable and perfect [in His plan and purpose for you].

I must admit I am a bit of a nerd, I love to see how the bible is practical and supports not only science, but neuroscience. This verse is a blueprint on how you change your thinking on a daily basis to develop neuroplasticity, growth mindset, a new neural pathway, which in turns create the new you, the you that is following God's plan for you. But you are not only following this plan, you are actually believing that this plan is possible for you and you can actually see it coming to life.

What are your thoughts on the Message Bible's translation of Romans 12:2?

Based on Romans 12:2, I created the RENNEW Framework, which you will go through in order to create your new mind to develop the life that God has for you.

RENNEW Framework ©

R – Reveal and Define

Reveal and define the vision God has for your life.

E – Explore what's holding you back

Explore what has been holding you back, keeping you stuck and getting in the way of you walking in your true vision.

N – Nurture the Vision

Nurture the vision by layering what this vision looks like for you. Its kind of like creating a 3D version of a vision board. Doing this will help you shape your reality.

N – Need to Believe

The need to believe in the RENNEW Framework is crucial. In order for you to move and not continue to get stuck you have to believe, you have to have faith in the unseen.

E – Establish Your Personal Blueprint

Establish your personal blueprint is creating your daily, practical plan for renewing your mind, and creating new neural pathways that will create your new future.

W – Work Your Blueprint

Work your blueprint is the part of the framework where you walk out and put into practice the work that you've done so far. This process will take at least 67 days.

Over the next chapters, we will dig deeper into each one of these areas to help you shape the life that God has revealed to you. Now God's desire for all of us is to be in a relationship with him. In our relationship with him, we learn to trust him in all areas of our lives because we know that he loves us. In being able to rest in that love and trust that he wants whats best for us no matter the situation or the circumstance will give you the peace that you've been longing for because you will be willing to do as the song says surrender all. You will give it to God and not try to take it back at the last minute because you don't trust that he will come through or you feel like you just can't let go of control. To help break down the ability to renew our lives even further, I have segmented different areas of our lives so that you can become focused in the area specifically that may need to be renewed and not waste energy on those areas that don't require your attention at least not at this time. The Soul Care Inventory is how you will be able to assess each area of your life in segments.

The Soul Care Inventory ©

Personal Growth and Development (intellectual)

This area takes into account what you do to grow personally and intellectually. This domain is responsible for your growth as a person and what steps you take to become the best version of yourself. The best woman.

Mental Health

You have a plan for your thought life. You are in control of your thoughts and how they impact how you feel and behave. When your thoughts begin to take a negative turn, you know how to stop your negative thoughts and replace them with new ones. You are able to consistently replace whatever negative lies you may tell yourself with the truth. You feel mentally stable.

Emotional Health

You have a plan for your emotional health. You are in control of your emotions and they do not control your thoughts and behaviors. You are able to pinpoint when your emotions are not aligned with the situation. You are able to display emotions that match what is going on. You can detect when you may be feeling down, depressed or anxious and you have the tools to work through those emotions.

Spiritual Health

You have a relationship with God. You have a connection with God. You believe that God loves you in all areas of your life. You believe that you trust God in all areas of your life. You have a way of connecting with God either through prayer, meditation, reading your bible, etc and you do this consistently. You are able to recognize and feel God's presence in your life and see it as a guiding light for you.

The Soul Care Inventory ©

Physical Health

You have a regular regimen to take care of your physical health that includes: your nutrition, physical activity, exercise, water intake, rest and. You schedule and keep annual doctor's appointments. You are aware of your physical health status and are taking necessary steps to improve or maintain a healthy lifestyle. You limit the intake of food, drinks, substances that tear down the full health of your body.

Financial Health

You are financially secure and have set plans in place to secure your financial future. You have financial goals that come from a place of abundance and not scarcity. You realize that money is a means to an end and not the end. Your relationship to money is not toxic. You can recognize if you become too focused on money and are able to put money in the proper perspective. Having and sharing money with others in need is a priority for you. You are able to financially share with others who God may lead you to help without feeling financially deprived.

Career and Business

You feel like you are on the right path for your career or business. You are in a career or have a business that uses the gifts and talents that God has given you. The time that you spend here is filling for you and brings light to you. You are able to operate in grace here and it is not a grind. You see how your career and business is a part of God's plan for your life.

Partner / Romance

You are happy with the relationship you have with your partner. You and your partner are connected physically, emotionally and spiritually. You enjoy spending time with your partner. The relationship with your partner is filled with love. You are fulfilled in your relationship with your partner. You are good partners to each other.

Fun/ Recreation/ Hobbies

You have activities that you like to do for fun that bring you enjoyment and it is not predicated on others. You enjoy your life and are able to have fun. You take part in hobbies that you enjoy. Others do not have to be involved in order for you to have fun in this activity. You engage in things that interest you and you are passionate about.

Physical Environment (work and home)

The physical space in your home and work environment brings you a sense of peace. You don't find these spaces stressful. These spaces are free from clutter. Your physical space is organized and you are able to enjoy the space as you intended.

The Soul Care Inventory ©

Social Support (Family and Friends)

These are your relationships with friends and family. You have a good social support system. You have people that you can count on and they provide you with emotional support. The relationships you have with friends and family are nourishing to you. You are able to support them in the same way they support you. You have a circle of people who support you through good and bad times. You feel connected to these people.

Parenting

You are parenting from a place that is nurturing. You are a loving parent. You are the kind of parent who is supportive of your children. You are a parent that provides structure, direction and discipline. You have a relationship with each of your children. You are happy with the way you are parenting your children. You are happy with the people they are growing into.

Rest Quality

You are able to take the time to rest. Your rest is peaceful. You are not anxious or restless in your sleep. Your rest is refreshing and not draining. You are able to take time away from others to create a peaceful space. You are able to quiet your mind and your body and be in a peaceful state. Your environment provides a sense of peace for you. You can withdraw from others to get rest. You are able to withdraw from the digital space and you are able to find peace with your digital space. You are able to let go and rest in each of these areas of your life in the soul care inventory, because you know that God loves you and wants what's best for you at all times and you trust him in that. You have peace.

Overall Quality of Life

You are pleased with where your life is at this point. You like the direction that your life is headed. You have the tools to keep your life on track. You enjoy your life and the people who are a part of your life. You enjoy the space that you live in. You are pleased with how you spend your days and are excited for your future. You are living your life according to how you want to live it. You are living a life of rest, peace and abundance.

Vision / Purpose / Contribution

You know the higher purpose for your life. You have a vision of how you see your life going. In 10 years, your future self will be pleased with the direction your life is headed. You are investing in living your life to the fullest in all areas. You are contributing to others and it is a part of your vision for your life and is in line with your purpose. You have a plan to achieve your best life. You are ready to live your life according to your vision and purpose and contribute to others with this gift.

In the next chapter you will work through the (R) of RENNEW, where you will Reveal and Define the life that you believe God is calling you to. If you think about anything you've done that has required more effort than one day's work to acquire that goal, you know it takes focus on the end result. Like Steven Covey says in *7 Habits of Highly Effective People,* begin with the end in mind. So in the next chapter we will begin with the end in mind - the end that God sees for you.

Commitment:

1. Meditate on Romans 12:2.
2. Pray and ask God to reveal to you how he wants to work this scripture out in your life
3. Write what you hear in the area below or in the answered prayer section in the back of the book. Make sure that you date the journal entry and which chapter it relates to.
4. If you haven't already, invite a sister, a friend, your small group, or colleagues to join you on this journey. Having someone to not only support you, but hold you accountable significantly improves the likelihood that you will accomplish your goal.

Write your commitment here:

Prayer:

Ask God to speak to you as you move through these next chapters and to speak to you and guide you in the areas in your life that he feels need to look more like him and the plans that he has for you. Ask God to give you the grace and the strength to move through the chapters so that you can become the woman that you know he has meant for you to be. Ask God to open your mind to new possibilities in him and expand your vision for yourself based on how he sees you.

Write your prayer below:

CHAPTER 5

Reveal and Define

Reveal and Define

We're going to start with a visualization here so that you can envision the life you believe God wants you to lead. You can read through the visualization here. I suggest you take the time to find a quiet place where you can listen to the visualization and answer the questions that follow. Listen very carefully as you go through the visualization to hear the voice of God. You can listen to the visualization here: www.soulcarebooks.com

We will use Ephesians 2:10 as our guidepost for the vision that God has for you

Visualization

Before you start, pray and ask God to show up during the visualization and speak to, tell you what he wants you to know, hear, feel, sense. Ask God to share his wisdom with you as you enter this space.

Trust God to show up and share his heart and his love for you as you go through this exercise.

Sit back and relax, find a comfortable place where you can relax with no distractions, Close your eyes and take a few deep breaths in. Take a deep breath in and now slowly exhale. Take another deep breath in and slowly exhale. One last time take a deep breath in and now slowly exhale. Now gradually relax your body from the top of your head, now your forehead. Relax the muscles in your face. Relax your jawline, allow your tongue to relax in your mouth. Now relax your shoulders, your arms, relax your hands. Now relax your chest and take another deep breath. Relax your stomach muscles. Your upper body should start to feel heavy. Allow it to feel heavy. Now relax your butt, your thighs, your calves, your ankles and now your feet. Continue to breathe deeply and slowly as you do. Allow your body to be completely relaxed. Now continue to take deep breaths. Slow down your breathing so that you can feel your breath as it goes in and your chest rises and then exhale. Feel your body continue to feel relaxed and heavy. Release all the tension from your body as you continue to take deep breaths in and then deep breaths out. As you are allowing your body to relax, imagine that you are going to a place to meet someone.

You are excited to meet them. You are anticipating meeting them because they have something for you. You enter this place and you are face to face with you in 20 years. Look at her. Can you see her? What does it feel like to be with her? What does she look like? What is she wearing? Where are you? What smells do you smell? What sounds do you hear? Does she serve you anything to eat or drink? Imagine that she is talking to you and wants to impart some wisdom or even a gift. What gift did she have to give you? What wisdom does she share with you? What does she say to you about your life now? What does she thank you for doing for her that has made your life easier and more peaceful in the future? Who is she?

What feeling or sense do you get from her? Ask her, how does she know the path, the vision, the calling that God has on your life? Now ask her anything else you want to know. Take some time to listen to her. Imagine that God is using her to speak to you. What does He want her to say to you? Listen carefully. Take it in. It's time to leave her now. How do you feel? I know you may not be ready to leave, but she is still with you. For now, say your goodbyes. Even though you may not want to leave, you have peace because she has shared what gives you peace. It's time for you to get up and gather your things to leave. What are you taking with you? What are you leaving there for her? How do you say goodbye to one another?

Begin to walk out the door. Move towards the place where you started. As you are moving, breathe in and then breathe out. Breathe in again and then breathe out. Once more breathe in and breathe out. Completely relax and open your eyes slowly. Take a deep breath as you open your eyes and just take a moment to sit with what you just saw, heard, and felt. Take it all in. Absorb all of it and be fully present with it.

Describe in detail what you saw in the visualization:

What did you smell in the visualization?

Where were you?

Describe what it looked like?

www.soulcarebooks.com

What sounds do you hear?

Who was there?

Describe in detail what she looked like?

www.soulcarebooks.com

How did she speak to you? How was her tone?

Does she serve you anything to eat or drink? What is it?

How does it feel to be with her?

www.soulcarebooks.com

What gift did she have to give you?

What wisdom does she share with you?

What does she say to you about your life now?

What does she thank you for doing for her that has made your life easier and more peaceful in the future?

Ask her, how does she know the path, the vision, the calling that God has on your life?

God is using her to speak to you. What does He want her to say to you?

As you leave, what are you taking with you?

What are you leaving there for her?

How do you say goodbye to one another?

Did you sense that she felt pleased with how your life has turned out or did it feel like she was angry or disappointed? Why?

As you move out of the time you spent with her, you should have a sense of who she was and how your life moving forward can look closer to hers. Answer the following questions to give you a clearer picture of what your life can look like.

www.soulcarebooks.com

What are some of her rituals- morning or evening routines?

How does she handle difficult relationships?

How does she handle money?

What kind of art or entertainment does she like?

How does she care for herself physically?

What does she eat?

How does she take care of herself emotionally?

www.soulcarebooks.com

How does she take care of herself mentally?

What does she do to take care of herself spiritually?

What kind of environment does she live and work in?

If there was a woman in the bible, in your life or a woman you admire that most aligns with this vision of yourself, who is it and why? Is it just one woman or a combination of women? Explain below:

What is it about her or them that you see as aligning with who you saw in this visualization?

www.soulcarebooks.com

What characteristics did she display?

What are her beliefs?

What does she value?

How does she honor God?

Where is her sweet spot?

How does this vision align with who you believe God has called you to , your sweet spot?

Does this vision allow you to use all of who God made you to be? How?

Write your bio based on this vision and the identity that God has shown you:

www.soulcarebooks.com

Write yourself two notes either in here or get two note cards.

- The first note is a thank you note to yourself from your perspective 5-10 years from now if you are fully walking in this vision - this identity. This identity you are writing from is the version of yourself where you are living at a level 10. A life of abundance in all areas of your life. Date the note with the date that you are writing the note and hold you are now. Then in the note write what year it will be in 5-10 years and how old you will be then.

- The second note is an apology letter to yourself 5 10 years from now if you did not take on this vision/identity. Write about what you'll regret and why you didn't take the necessary steps to move into this vision. Date the note with the date that you are writing the note and hold you are now. Then in the note write what year it will be in 5-10 years and how old you will be then.

Commitment:

1. Meditate on Ephesians 2:10.
2. Pray and ask God to reveal to you how he wants to work this scripture out in your life.
3. Write what you hear in the area below or in the answered prayer section in the back of the book. Make sure that you date the journal entry and which chapter it relates to.
4. Commit to going through and being fully present while doing the visualization. Complete the work surrounding the visualization.

Write your commitment here:

Prayer:

Ask God to show you the vision that He has for your life. Ask God to use your own life as an inspiration for you moving forward and to draw you closer to the woman He wants you to be. Thank God for showing you His vision.

Write your prayer below:

Chapter 6

Explore What's Holding You Back

EXPLORE WHAT'S HOLDING YOU BACK

In this area we will look at what has been holding you back. We will look at what are the thoughts, feelings, behaviors, habits, values, beliefs, expectations and identity that have been holding you back from a life full of abundance. We will determine which areas are out of alignment and which areas are stealing your joy. This area is in-depth and will cause you to stretch and really think. Please don't skip this area even though it may be very uncomfortable at times. You may even feel like putting the book down telling yourself that you didn't buy the book for this, this is too hard, or whatever the negative tape is that you play whenever something gets too hard or makes you uncomfortable. This is just another way that your brain is trying to keep you safe. But I want you to push through so that you can get to the other side. Agreed? Ok now let's dive in. In this section, you will explore the issues that are causing exhaustion, stress, anxiety, for you. Below you will find a list of questions I want you to answer to uncover these. This area is like when you go to your dr's office or your therapist's office and they ask, what has brought you in today? What's your presenting issue? What's the issue that is causing you the most stress? We want to define this clearly so that we can create a plan to work through it.

What are the issues that have caused you to feel stressed at this point in your life?

What causes you the most stress?

What has caused you anxiety?

When you think about the thing or the person that causes you the most stress, what is it? Why is it so stressful?

What happened to bring you to the point where you want to change the thing causing you the stress?

Why is it so important now?

What will happen if you don't start now?

On a scale of 1-10, with 1 being the lowest and 10 being the highest, rate how you see your life in each of the areas of the soul care domains.

 If you need a reminder of the definition for each please refer back to Chapter 4.(Put a date next to your score so that you can track your progress.)

Soul Care Inventory

Name	Score	Date
Personal Growth and Development (intellectual)		
Mental Health		
Emotional Health		
Spiritual Health		
Physical Health		
Financial Health		
Career and Business		
Partner / Romance		
Fun/ Recreation/ Hobbies		
Physical Environment (work and home)		
Social Support (Family and Friends)		
Parenting		
Rest Quality		
Overall Quality of Life		
Vision / Purpose / Contribution		

Below is an example of how to complete the Soul Care Inventory:

Name	Score	Date
Personal Growth and Development (intellectual)	7	2/25/20
Mental Health	6	2/25/20
Emotional Health	3	2/25/20
Spiritual Health	5	2/25/20
Physical Health	4	2/25/20
Financial Health	8	2/25/20
Career and Business	6	2/25/20
Partner/ Romance	7	2/25/20
Fun/ Recreation/ Hobbies	6	2/25/20
Physical Environment (work and home)	8	2/25/20
Social Support (Family and Friends)	8	2/25/20
Parenting	6	2/25/20
Rest Quality	4	2/25/20
Overall Quality of Life	6	2/25/20
Vision / Purpose / Contribution	3	2/25/20

Now for each area, I want you to answer why you believe you have rated it that number.

For example, from the chart above, Rest Quality was rated at a 4 because I don't get enough sleep on a daily basis and I wake up in the middle of the night worrying about my physical health because I haven't been feeling well lately.

After answering this question there will be a series of questions on each area to gauge how you see yourself, the role your beliefs, habits and behaviors in each area play in your life. Finally, there is a question that will help you identify the role you believe God plays in each of these areas in your life.

We all have certain behaviors that begin to form into habits that we may not even be aware of, but they help to shape our identity in these areas and some of the main culprits in keeping us living below where we want to be.

Now you do the same for each category below:

1.**Personal Growth and Development (intellectual)** - This area takes into account what you do to grow personally and intellectually. This domain is responsible for your growth as a person and what steps you take to become the best version of yourself. The best woman. You incorporate strategies to continue to learn and grow.

I rated Personal Growth and Development (intellectual) at a _____ because:

What are your feelings about Personal Growth and Development (intellectual)? What do you value about Personal Growth and Development (intellectual)?

How do you implement Personal Growth and Development (intellectual) in your life? What are the expectations that you have for yourself in this area?

What are your beliefs in this area? Who do you see yourself as in this area (how do you identify yourself here)?

What are your habits in this area?

Are any of your beliefs, habits or how you identify yourself in this area holding you back?

Do you fully trust God in this area? Why or why not?

2. **Mental Health** - You have a plan for your thought life. You are in control of your thoughts and how they impact how you feel and behave. When your thoughts begin to take a negative turn, you know how to stop your negative thoughts and replace them with new ones. You are able to consistently replace whatever negative lies you may tell yourself with the truth. You feel mentally stable.

I rated Mental Health at a _____ because:

What are your feelings about Mental Health ? What do you value about Mental Health?

How do you implement Mental Health in your life? What are the expectations that you have for yourself in this area?

What are your beliefs in this area? Who do you see yourself as in this area (how do you identify yourself here)?

What are your habits in this area?

Are any of your beliefs, habits or how you identify yourself in this area holding you back?

Do you fully trust God in this area? Why or why not?

3. Emotional Health - You have a plan for your emotional health. You are in control of your emotions and they do not control your thoughts and behaviors. You are able to pinpoint when your emotions are not aligned with the situation. You are able to display emotions that match what is going on. You can detect when you may be feeling down, depressed or anxious and you have the tools to work through those emotions.

I rated Emotional Health at a _____ because:

What are your feelings about Emotional Health ? What do you value about Emotional Health?

How do you implement Emotional Health in your life? What are the expectations that you have for yourself in this area?

What are your beliefs in this area? Who do you see yourself as in this area (how do you identify yourself here)?

What are your habits in this area?

Are any of your beliefs, habits or how you identify yourself in this area holding you back?

Do you fully trust God in this area? Why or why not?

4. Spiritual Health - You have a relationship with God. You have a connection with God. You believe that God loves you in all areas of your life. You believe that you trust God in all areas of your life. You have a way of connecting with God either through prayer, meditation, reading your bible, etc and you do this consistently. You are able to recognize and feel God's presence in your life and see it as a guiding light for you.

I rated Spiritual Health at a _____ because:

What are your feelings about Spiritual Health? What do you value about Spiritual Health?

How do you implement Spiritual Health in your life? What are the expectations that you have for yourself in this area?

What are your beliefs in this area? Who do you see yourself as in this area (how do you identify yourself here)?

What are your habits in this area?

Are any of your beliefs, habits or how you identify yourself in this area holding you back?

Do you fully trust God in this area? Why or why not?

5. Physical Health - You have a regular regimen to take care of your physical health that includes: your nutrition, physical activity, exercise, water intake, rest and proper medical care. You schedule and keep annual doctor's appointments. You are aware of your physical health status and are taking necessary steps to improve or maintain a healthy lifestyle. You limit the intake of food, drinks, substances that tear down the full health of your body.

I rated Physical Health at a _____ because:

What are your feelings about Physical Health? What do you value about Physical Health?

How do you implement Physical Health in your life? What are the expectations that you have for yourself in this area?

What are your beliefs in this area? Who do you see yourself as in this area (how do you identify yourself here)?

What are your habits in this area?

Are any of your beliefs, habits or how you identify yourself in this area holding you back?

Do you fully trust God in this area? Why or why not?

6. Financial Health- You are financially secure and have set plans in place to secure your financial future. You have financial goals that come from a place of abundance and not scarcity. You realize that money is a means to an end and not the end. Your relationship to money is not toxic. You can recognize if you become too focused on money and are able to put money in the proper perspective. Having and sharing money with others in need is a priority for you. You are able to financially share with others who God may lead you to help without feeling financially deprived.

I rated Financial Health at a _ _ _ _ _ _ because:

What are your feelings about Financial Health? What do you value about Finaces?

How do you implement Financial Health in your life? What are the expectations that you have for yourself in this area?

What are your beliefs in this area? Who do you see yourself as in this area (how do you identify yourself here)?

What are your habits in this area?

Are any of your beliefs, habits or how you identify yourself in this area holding you back?

Do you fully trust God in this area? Why or why not?

7. Career and Business - You feel like you are on the right path for your career or business. You are in a career or have a business that uses the gifts and talents that God has given you. The time that you spend here is filling for you and brings light to you. You are happy with the work you get to share with the world. You feel a sense of accomplishment with the work that you do. It is a part or your sweet spot. You are able to operate in grace here and it is not a grind. You see how your career and business is a part of God's plan for your life.

I rated Career and Business at a _____ because:

What are your feelings about your Career and Business? What do you value about Career and Business?

How do you implement your thoughts about success in Career and Business in your life? What are the expectations that you have for yourself in this area?

What are your beliefs in this area? Who do you see yourself as in this area (how do you identify yourself here)?

What are your habits in this area?

Are any of your beliefs, habits or how you identify yourself in this area holding you back?

Do you fully trust God in this area? Why or why not?

www.soulcarebooks.com

8. Partner / Romance - You are happy with the relationship you have with your partner. You and your partner are connected physically, emotionally and spiritually. You enjoy spending time with your partner. The relationship with your partner is filled with love. You are fulfilled in your relationship with your partner. You are good partners to each other.

I rated Partner / Romance at a _____ because:

What are your feelings about Partner / Romance? What do you value about Partner / Romance?

How do you implement a healthy Partner / Romance relationship in your life? What are the expectations that you have for yourself in this area?

What are your beliefs in this area? Who do you see yourself as in this area (how do you identify yourself here)?

What are your habits in this area?

Are any of your beliefs, habits or how you identify yourself in this area holding you back?

Do you fully trust God in this area? Why or why not?

www.soulcarebooks.com

9. Fun/ Recreation/ Hobbies - You have activities that you like to do for fun that bring you enjoyment and it is not predicated on others. You enjoy your life and are able to have fun. You take part in hobbies that you enjoy. Others do not have to be involved in order for you to have fun in this activity. You engage in things that interest you and you are passionate about.

I rated Fun/ Recreation/ Hobbies at a _____ because:

What are your feelings about Fun/ Recreation/ Hobbies? What do you value about Fun/ Recreation/ Hobbies?

How do you implement Fun/ Recreation/ Hobbies in your life? What are the expectations that you have for yourself in this area?

What are your beliefs in this area? Who do you see yourself as in this area (how do you identify yourself here)?

What are your habits in this area?

Are any of your beliefs, habits or how you identify yourself in this area holding you back?

www.soulcarebooks.com

Do you fully trust God in this area? Why or why not?

10. Physical Environment (work and home) - The physical space in your home and work environment brings you a sense of peace. You don't find these spaces stressful. These spaces are free from clutter. Your physical space is organized and you are able to enjoy the space as you intended.

I rated Physical Environment (work and home) at a _ _ _ _ _ _ because:

What are your feelings about your Physical Environment (work and home)? What do you value about Physical Environment (work and home)?

How do you create the Physical Environment (work and home) you desire in your life? What are the expectations that you have for yourself in this area?

What are your beliefs in this area? Who do you see yourself as in this area (how do you identify yourself here)?

What are your habits in this area?

Are any of your beliefs, habits or how you identify yourself in this area holding you back?

Do you fully trust God in this area? Why or why not?

11. Social Support (Family and Friends) - These are your relationships with friends and family. You have a good social support system. You have people that you can count on and they provide you with emotional support. The relationships you have with friends and family are nourishing to you. You are able to support them in the same way they support you. You have a circle of people who support you through good and bad times. You feel connected to these people.

I rated Social Support (Family and Friends) at a _____ because:

What are your feelings about Social Support (Family and Friends)? What do you value about Social Support (Family and Friends)?

How do you incorporate your Social Support (Family and Friends) in your life? What are the expectations that you have for yourself in this area?

What are your beliefs in this area? Who do you see yourself as in this area (how do you identify yourself here)?

What are your habits in this area?

Are any of your beliefs, habits or how you identify yourself in this area holding you back?

www.soulcarebooks.com

Do you fully trust God in this area? Why or why not?

12. Parenting - You are parenting from a place that is nurturing. You are a loving parent. You are the kind of parent who is supportive of your children. You are a parent that provides structure, direction and discipline. You are able to communicate and show your love to your children. You have a relationship with each of your children. You are happy with the way you are parenting your children. You are happy with the people they are growing into. Your children are blessed to have you as a parent.

I rated Parenting at a _____ because:

www.soulcarebooks.com

What are your feelings about Parenting? What do you value about Parenting?

How do you incorporate Parenting in your life? What are the expectations that you have for yourself in this area?

What are your beliefs in this area? Who do you see yourself as in this area (how do you identify yourself here)?

What are your habits in this area?

Are any of your beliefs, habits or how you identify yourself in this area holding you back?

Do you fully trust God in this area? Why or why not?

13. Rest Quality - You are able to take the time to rest. Your rest is peaceful. You are not anxious or restless in your sleep. Your rest is refreshing and not draining. You are able to take time away from others to create a peaceful space. You are able to quiet your mind and your body and be in a peaceful state. Your environment provides a sense of peace for you. You can withdraw from others to get rest. You are able to withdraw from the digital space and you are able to find peace with your digital space. You are able to let go and rest in each of these areas of your life in the soul care inventory, because you know that God loves you and wants what's best for you at all times and you trust him in that. You have peace.

I rated Rest Quality at a _ _ _ _ _ _ because:

What are your feelings about Rest Quality? What do you value about Rest Quality?

How do you incorporate Rest Quality in your life? What are the expectations that you have for yourself in this area?

What are your beliefs in this area? Who do you see yourself as in this area (how do you identify yourself here)?

What are your habits in this area?

Are any of your beliefs, habits or how you identify yourself in this area holding you back?

Do you fully trust God in this area? Why or why not?

www.soulcarebooks.com

14. Overall Quality of Life - You are pleased with where your life is at this point. You like the direction that your life is headed. You have the tools to keep your life on track. You enjoy your life and the people who are a part of your life. You enjoy the space that you live in. You are pleased with how you spend your days and are excited for your future. You are living your life according to how you want to live it. You are living a life of rest, peace and abundance.

I rated Overall Quality of Life at a _____ because:

What are your feelings about your Overall Quality of Life? What do you value about your Overall Quality of Life?

What are the expectations that you have for yourself in this area?

What are your beliefs in this area? Who do you see yourself as in this area (how do you identify yourself here)?

What are your habits in this area?

Are any of your beliefs, habits or how you identify yourself in this area holding you back?

Do you fully trust God in this area? Why or why not?

15. Vision / Purpose / Contribution - You know the higher purpose for your life. You have a vision of how you see your life going. In 10 years, your future self will be pleased with the direction your life is headed. You are investing in living your life to the fullest in all areas. You are contributing to others and it is a part of your vision for your life and is in line with your purpose. You have a plan to achieve your best life. You are ready to live your life according to your vision and purpose and contribute to others with this gift.

I rated Vision / Purpose / Contribution at a _____ because:

What are your feelings about Vision / Purpose / Contribution? What do you value about Vision / Purpose / Contribution?

How do you implement Vision / Purpose / Contribution in your life? What are the expectations that you have for yourself in this area?

What are your beliefs in this area? Who do you see yourself as in this area (how do you identify yourself here)?

What are your habits in this area?

Are any of your beliefs, habits or how you identify yourself in this area holding you back?

Do you fully trust God in this area? Why or why not?

Which of three areas according to your ranks cause you the most stress?

[ ]

Which areas are stealing your peace, your joy, your abundance?

[ ]

In this scenario, vision/purpose/contribution is the lowest category, then physical health and rest quality. Because vision was the lowest this would be the area that would be addressed first.

Look at your list and write your answers here. Then rank them according to their score. The category with the lowest score would be ranked #1, the next lowest score is ranked #2 and then the score right above this one will be ranked #3.

Now, look at your top 3 issues and rank them in order of priority with the one with the highest priority being ranked #1. In doing this, you are saying that the #1 issue is the one you will work on first and if you deal with this issue, it can help to bring other issues in alignment.

Example:

Rank	Name	Score	Date
1	Vision / Purpose / Contribution	3	2/25/20
2	Physical Health	4	2/25/20
3	Rest Quality	4	2/25/20

What were your lowest 3?

Rank	Name	Score	Date
1			
2			
3			

Write below why you believe these three areas are causing you the most stress or are robbing you of your peace of mind?

What's the #1 issue causing you stress? Why?

Do you trust God in these areas? Why or why not?

Now let's look at the areas that bring you the most joy and the most peace.

Which three areas according to your ratings give you the most joy and peace?

Example:

Rank	Name	Score	Date
1	Physical Environment	8	2/25/20
2	Financial Health	8	2/25/20
3	Social Support	8	2/25/20

In this scenario, physical environment, finances and social support brought the most joy and peace.

Look at your list. What areas give you the most joy and peace? Then rank these areas and write your answers here:

Rank	Name	Score	Date
1			
2			
3			

Write below why you believe these three areas are giving you the most joy, contributing to a life of abundance and giving you peace.

Are you showing up differently in these areas than the three that are causing you stress? If so, how?

What are some of the themes and patterns that are showing up in the three areas that bring you the most joy and peace?

Do you behave differently in these areas than you do in the lowest three? If so how?

Do you trust God in these areas? Why or why not?

www.soulcarebooks.com

I know it may feel like I just got all up in your business, but I promise you, I have no idea what you wrote. I know for some of you reading this, that is a great relief. But seriously, CONGRATULATIONS on completing this section. It is a long section and it digs deeply in how you feel in each area. I do this so that you can see where you are now in order to plan for what you want and what God has planned for you. This book is all about discovering those areas that have been getting in your way, seeing God's vision and then being very intentional about getting there.

So how do you move from here? This is what we will deal with in the next section. Now at this point you may be starting to feel a little fatigued or even a little overwhelmed. Take a break, whatever that looks like for you - a few hours or a few days. But make sure you come back because the next section will deal with how you can begin to create the vision for your life at the level you know you should be living.

Commitment:

1. Complete the Soul Care Inventory. Answer each question. If there were any questions that you skipped, go back and answer, then examine why you skipped it.
2. Be as thorough in this area as possible. You will refer back to this area in the future and you will be able to see the progress that you have made.
3. Take time to reward yourself after going through this work. This is an incentive to help you keep going.

Write your commitment here:

Prayer:

Ask God to help you reveal the truth about what's been holding you back. Ask God to help you understand the areas that have been keeping you stuck. Ask God to help you move forward and not get overwhelmed, discouraged or stuck here. Know that God has a plan for you and loves you no matter the answers you gave above. He loves every part of you and wants you to look more like Him. Ask God to reveal His love for you even in those areas you feel are really out of alignment with who He says that you are.

Write your prayer below:

www.soulcarebooks.com

CHAPTER 7

Write the Vision

&

Make it Plain

WRITE THE VISION & MAKE IT PLAIN

In the last chapter, we dealt with the areas that have been holding you back. Hopefully, you were able to pinpoint the top three areas that you will deliberately focus on when we get to the planner section of this journal.

In this chapter, you will go on a journey to nurturing the vision that you saw in Chapter 5. Go back and read through those answers to help you complete the questions in this chapter.

In Habakkuk 2:2, it states, write the vision and make it plain, so that is exactly what you will do in this chapter. In as much detail as you put in chapters 5 and 6, I want you to put the same detail here. Remember, this journal is for you. Think of this journal as your own personal roadmap to the life that God has in store for you. A big part of sustaining the momentum and the desire to want to meet the goal is to layer it with the sights, sounds and smells to the point that it almost forms a memory before you have even created it.

Let me explain. Have you ever done a vision board? A vision board is a flat or 2D version of your vision. What I'm asking you to do in this chapter is what I like to call nurturing the vision. In doing this, you will layer in the attributes of your vision that can and will bring it to life. The details that will make it 3D.

Think about a time that brings back a great memory. What do you notice about that memory?

Write it here:

What you can see from this exercise is that a memory entails more than what you did. It also entails what you saw, what you heard, what you smelled, what you touched, maybe even what you tasted. A layered memory encompasses your five senses and then some. This is why there are times you will hear a song or smell a cologne or perfume and it will remind you instantly of a certain time in your life. You immediately go into a flashback. This effect is what you will be doing with the layering here. You will be layering in not just the vision, but the experience of that vision so that you will be pulled towards it, even compelled to move towards it. It will call to you when you try to put it down because you will be drawn to making this experience a reality. You may have already done some of this in dreaming about how you want your life to look and that may be why you picked up this book in the first place because you know that you are called to more.

Let's get started layering.

Soul Care Vision Inventory

Now that you have a sense of the life that you can be leading, look again at the domains of soul care to answer the following questions:

These next sections are why vision boards and New Year's Resolutions don't work. If you want to finally move forward and keep your vision your goal, learn to write the vision and make it plain.

In each area from the last chapter what does a 10 life look like, we've defined that as what a Rested, renewed and abundant life looks like for you. Describe in as much detail as possible. Get pictures in your head, get visual reminders that you can paste in this section of the book.

This vision of who God sees you as and who you see yourself as is a very personal vision. Let me free you here, it's not what others believe that you should be or look like, it's who God says you are and then shares with you what that looks like. Only you and God truly know who that is for you. Others may have a glimpse but they don't truly know so you have to trust God and use discernment so that you can also learn to trust your own judgement.

In Chapter 5, you answered in your gut where you saw your life in each area on a scale of 1-10, with 1 being the lowest and 10 being the highest. If you were able to rate each area then on some level, you have an idea of what your life could look like on the highest level in each of these areas. Keep this in mind when completing the Soul Care Inventory now. If you lived your life on the highest level, a level 10, what would each area look like?

If you lived your life on the level that you know God is calling you to, what would each area look like?

Personal Growth and Development (intellectual) - If this represented a 10, how would you answer these questions?

This area takes into account what you do to grow personally and intellectually. This domain is responsible for your growth as a person and what steps you take to become the best version of yourself. The best woman. You incorporate strategies to continue to learn and grow.

What does this area look like if you lived in on the highest level, a level 10? What would this area look like if you lived it on the level that God has intended you to live.

Describe what that looks like here:

Mental Health If this represented a 10, what would your life look like?

You have a plan for your thought life. You are in control of your thoughts and how they impact how you feel and behave. When your thoughts begin to take a negative turn, you know how to stop your negative thoughts and replace them with new ones. You are able to consistently replace whatever negative lies you may tell yourself with the truth. You feel mentally stable.

What does this area look like if you lived in on the highest level, a level 10? What would this area look like if you lived it on the level that God has intended you to live.

Describe what that looks like here:

[blank box]

Emotional Health If this represented a 10, how would you answer these questions?

You have a plan for your emotional health. You are in control of your emotions and they do not control your thoughts and behaviors. You are able to pinpoint when your emotions are not aligned with the situation. You are able to display emotions that match what is going on. You can detect when you may be feeling down, depressed or anxious and you have the tools to work through those emotions.

What does this area look like if you lived in on the highest level, a level 10? What would this area look like if you lived it on the level that God has intended you to live.

Describe what that looks like here:

[blank box]

Spiritual Health If this represented a 10, how would you answer these questions?

You have a relationship with God. You have a connection with God. You believe that God loves you in all areas of your life. You believe that you trust God in all areas of your life. You have a way of connecting with God either through prayer, meditation, reading your bible, etc and you do this consistently. You are able to recognize and feel God's presence in your life and see it as a guiding light for you.

What does this area look like if you lived in on the highest level, a level 10? What would this area look like if you lived it on the level that God has intended you to live.

Describe what that looks like here:

Physical Health If this represented a 10, how would you answer these questions?

You have a regular regimen to take care of your physical health that includes - your nutrition, physical activity, exercise, water intake, rest and proper medical care. You schedule and keep annual doctor's appointments. You are aware of your physical health status and are taking necessary steps to improve or maintain a healthy lifestyle. You limit the intake of food, drinks, substances that tear down the full health of your body.

What does this area look like if you lived in on the highest level, a level 10? What would this area look like if you lived it on the level that God has intended you to live.

Describe what that looks like here:

[ ]

Financial Health If this represented a 10, how would you answer these questions?

You are financially secure and have set plans in place to secure your financial future. You have financial goals that come from a place of abundance and not scarcity. You realize that money is a means to an end and not the end. Your relationship to money is not toxic. You can recognize if you become too focused on money and are able to put money in the proper perspective. Having and sharing money with others in need is a priority for you. You are able to financially share with others who God may lead you to help without feeling financially deprived.

What does this area look like if you lived in on the highest level, a level 10? What would this area look like if you lived it on the level that God has intended you to live.

Describe what that looks like here:

[ ]

Career and Business If this represented a 10, how would you answer these questions?

You feel like you are on the right path for your career or business. You are in a career or have a business that uses the gifts and talents that God has given you. The time that you spend here is filling for you and brings light to you. You are happy with the work you get to share with the world. You feel a sense of accomplishment with the work that you do. It is a part or your sweet spot. You are able to operate in grace here and it is not a grind. You see how your career and business is a part of God's plan for your life.

What does this area look like if you lived in on the highest level, a level 10? What would this area look like if you lived it on the level that God has intended you to live.

Describe what that looks like here:

Partner/ Romance If this represented a 10, how would you answer these questions?

You are happy with the relationship you have with your partner. You and your partner are connected physically, emotionally and spiritually. You enjoy spending time with your partner. The relationship with your partner is filled with love. You are fulfilled in your relationship with your partner. You are good partners to each other.

What does this area look like if you lived in on the highest level, a level 10? What would this area look like if you lived it on the level that God has intended you to live.

Describe what that looks like here:

[ ]

Fun/ Recreation/ Hobbies If this represented a 10, how would you answer these questions?

You have activities that you like to do for fun that bring you enjoyment and it is not predicated on others. You enjoy your life and are able to have fun. You take part in hobbies that you enjoy. Others do not have to be involved in order for you to have fun in this activity. You engage in things that interest you and you are passionate about.

What does this area look like if you lived in on the highest level, a level 10? What would this area look like if you lived it on the level that God has intended you to live.

Describe what that looks like here:

[ ]

Physical Environment (work and home) If this represented a 10, how would you answer these questions?

The physical space in your home and work environment brings you a sense of peace. You don't find these spaces stressful. These spaces are free from clutter. Your physical space is organized and you are able to enjoy the space as you intended.

What does this area look like if you lived in on the highest level, a level 10? What would this area look like if you lived it on the level that God has intended you to live.

Describe what that looks like here:

Social Support (Family and Friends) If this represented a 10, how would you answer these questions?

These are your relationships with friends and family. You have a good social support system. You have people that you can count on and they provide you with emotional support.The relationships you have with friends and family are nourishing to you. You are able to support them in the same way they support you. You have a circle of people who support you through good and bad times. You feel connected to these people.

What does this area look like if you lived in on the highest level, a level 10? What would this area look like if you lived it on the level that God has intended you to live.

Describe what that looks like here:

[ ]

Parenting If this represented a 10, how would you answer these questions?

You are parenting from a place that is nurturing. You are a loving parent. You are the kind of parent who is supportive of your children. You are a parent that provides structure, direction and discipline. You are able to communicate and show your love to your children. You have a relationship with each of your children. You are happy with the way you are parenting your children. You are happy with the people they are growing into. Your children are blessed to have you as a parent.

What does this area look like if you lived in on the highest level, a level 10? What would this area look like if you lived it on the level that God has intended you to live.

Describe what that looks like here:

[ ]

Rest Quality If this represented a 10, how would you answer these questions?

You are able to take the time to rest. Your rest is peaceful. You are not anxious or restless in your sleep. Your rest is refreshing and not draining. You are able to take time away from others to create a peaceful space. You are able to quiet your mind and your body and be in a peaceful state. Your environment provides a sense of peace for you. You can withdraw from others to get rest. You are able to withdraw from your digital space and you are able to find peace with your digital space. You are able to let go and rest in each of these areas of your life in the soul care inventory, because you know that God loves you and wants what's best for you at all times and you trust him in that. You have peace.

What does this area look like if you lived in on the highest level, a level 10? What would this area look like if you lived it on the level that God has intended you to live.

Describe what that looks like here:

Overall Quality of Life If this represented a 10, how would you answer these questions?

You are pleased with where your life is at this point. You like the direction that your life is headed. You have the tools to keep your life on track. You enjoy your life and the people who are a part of your life. You enjoy the space that you live in. You are pleased with how you spend your days and are excited for your future. You are living your life according to how you want to live it. You are living a life of rest, peace and abundance.

What does this area look like if you lived in on the highest level, a level 10? What would this area look like if you lived it on the level that God has intended you to live.

Describe what that looks like here:

[ ]

Vision / Purpose / Contribution If this represented a 10, how would you answer these questions?

You know the higher purpose for your life. You have a vision of how you see your life going. In 10 years, your future self will be pleased with the direction your life is headed. You are investing in living your life to the fullest in all areas. You are contributing to others and it is a part of your vision for your life and is in line with your purpose. You have a plan to achieve your best life. You are ready to live your life according to your vision and purpose and contribute to others with this gift.

What does this area look like if you lived in on the highest level, a level 10? What would this area look like if you lived it on the level that God has intended you to live.

Describe what that looks like here:

[ ]

Who is the kind of person who achieves this type of life?

When you reach this level of success and happiness in your life, describe how will you feel below:

If this version of your life had a soundtrack, what songs would be part of it?

The reason that you will be successful in living this life this time is because:

Do you believe that you can live this type of life? Why or Why not?

What else do you see when you dream about this woman? Write it here:

How does it feel to have such a complete picture of who you and God believe you are? Just take in this moment and fully embrace what this moment feels like. Take a deep breath in and a deep breath out. If you are anything like me, you feel like a huge weight has been lifted off of your shoulders. You can actually visually see yourself exhaling and so much of your stress and worry going along with it. Breathe in again, hold it and breathe out.

The Final Layers

In this final step to layering, you will create ways that can be reminders for you of who this woman is so that you are drawn to her and so that she can be a reminder to you at the times when you may be pulled back.

In this section, I want you to create a vision board and a vision audio or vision video based on all of the work that you just did to layer your vision. You should have a clear picture of what your life looks like when you are living at your highest level 10.

You can either do your vision board digitally or take a poster board and cut out words, pictures, symbols, bible verses. Make it as elaborate as you want so that you can have a visual reminder of what your life looks like on 10.

Now to layer this even further you can look at each area of the Soul Care Inventory and get pictures, symbols, words and bible verses that support these areas. You can create a folder on your phone or in google drive, on your computer or a paper file folder and fill them with notes, articles, videos, sermons, podcasts, devotionals, to use that will support and encourage you to continue your vision.

Next create an audio where you completely describe your vision with all of its layers in as much detail as possible. You are doing this so that you will not only see your vision, but you will be able to listen in your own words to what the vision looks like to you. In the audio, speak as if it is already done.

If audio doesn't work for you, create a video with still images, video, music of the vision you have outlined. Again this video will act as an encouragement for you on a daily basis to build the belief in you and the excitement in you for the life you believe God has for you. Doing either the audio or video, in this way, puts you in the state of mind that this is already done and this will create a sense of gratitude.

Gratitude, remember, is one of those positive emotions that helps us create dopamine, serotonin, joy and happiness and draws us in to want more. Understand that being in a true place of gratefulness comes from the place or the belief that the thing you are experiencing is already done. You can't be in that space of gratefulness of it already being done, if you don't truly believe it.

Has there been a time that you experienced true gratitude for something that you believed was already done, but it had not yet come to pass?

How were you able to do this?

What was it about that situation that allowed you to have that state of being grateful even though you couldn't see it?

What do you think you can do to repeat this process in other areas of your life?

The need to believe or have faith leads us right into the next chapter, where we will dive into the Need to Believe section of the RENNEW Framework.

DON'T GET STUCK HERE

Some people get stuck in this area because everyone gets excited about what their life could look like especially if there is a large enough gap between the vision and where you are. Don't live here, Don't sit at the gate waiting like the beggar with his cup at the gate stuck between his present and his future, his current life and abundance. His created reality and God's vision for his life Acts 3:1-10.

This book is offering you a clear cut plan to not only make the vision, but a way to make, implement and sustain the plan.

In the next section, we'll move through the process of belief and how your belief / faith will impact the outcome of your vision.

Commitment:

1. Commit to meditating on Habakkuk 2:2
2. Ask God to continue to reveal his vision to you
3. Complete the exercises in this chapter
4. Nurture the vision by layering with a vision board, a vision audio and/or a vision video
5. Don't allow yourself to get stuck in the dreaming
6. Commit to moving forward and doing the work to attain this vision
7. Come back to update the vision as God continues to reveal it to you.

Write your commitment here:

Prayer:

Ask God to reveal his vision for you. Ask God to help you see the vision the way that he sees it. Pray that you recognize God's will in your life and that you know that he wants what's best for you even when circumstances may not look that way. Thank God in advance for bringing your vision to pass because your vision lines up with His vision for you. Thank God and worship him for fulfilling his vision in you and allowing you to fully be who you are in the fulfillment of that vision. Thank God that he allows every part of you to show up. Thank God that he is concerned about every part of your life because you are important to him and he loves you.

Write your prayer below:

CHAPTER 8

Need to Believe

NEED TO BELIEVE
Faith, Without Works is Dead- James 2:26

The beginning process of the RENNEW Framework © gives you an understanding of where you are now and where you see your life going according to what was revealed to you in the guided visualization and the work done afterwards to layer it. In this chapter, you will go a little deeper to truly shore up your faith muscles to grow your belief.

This area is where vision boards get put in the back of the closet and why goals are dropped. Everyone is so excited about the new year because they feel its a natural reset, but God gives a natural reset daily with Hebrews 12:2. Renew your mind. You have the opportunity every day to have a reset on how you see yourself and the world around you.

In this chapter, we'll discuss the second (N) in the RENNEW Framework; Need to Believe. Need to Believe is going beyond vision to true belief, belief in the vision for yourself in each area. Faith that your life can truly look like your vision.

In order for any new goal, concept or identity to be formed, you have to believe that it's possible, If you don't believe that it's true, there will be a disconnect. This is called cognitive dissonance. If there is a disconnect of belief, that goal won't be achieved because deep down you truly don't believe it. This concept is why when you made plans for something that is outside of your comfort zone, it can feel so hard to accomplish. It can feel like you have one foot on the gas and one foot on the brake. What happens if you do that? Nothing. You won't move. You're stuck.

This section will help you identify the things that are keeping your foot on the brake pedal so that we can remove them and replace them so that you can move. In this chapter, you will learn the tools to build your belief, your faith.

!WARNING!

I will be asking you to rewire parts of your brain that may have been this way for years. The way you think, feel and act in these areas may be deeply entrenched. However, they can be changed. You just have to put in the work.

DEATH AND LIFE ARE IN THE POWER OF THE TONGUE. Proverbs 18:21 NKJV

THE WAY YOU SPEAK TO YOURSELF, THE WAY YOU SPEAK OVER YOUR LIFE, THE EXPECTATIONS YOU SET FOR YOUR LIFE CAN EITHER SPEAK LIFE OR DEATH.

Fear to Faith Continuum

Fear and faith are on a continuum. The lesser the belief that you have in the vision God has for you, the closer you are to fear. The more belief that you have in the vision, the closer you are to faith. When you're in fear, it causes you to act out in fear.

<--->
Fear   Faith

Our brains are naturally wired to protect us so when we feel a sense of fear we run, fight or freeze. Fear comes from what you you tell yourself is true. Now this is an automatic process, but you can interrupt it. Let me explain. Our brains are wired to protect us. It is wired, at the most base level, to put things in boxes of harmful and not harmful. When something is seen as harmful, an alert happens in our brain and translates it into the fear response of fight, flight, or freeze. So anything that you perceive as scary, you will react with either running, fighting or just stopping in your tracks and freezing. Pause and let that sink in. Can you think of something in your life where this happens? What about when you have a new responsibility at work, whether you asked for it or not, how do you feel? How do you feel when you meet someone new after years of not dating anyone? How about the vision God has shared with you just in the pages of this book? How did you initially feel? This automatic response is designed to protect us from harm. The issue is when we allow that response to take over and remain stuck there and can't move on. Hence, in some instances, you know you want to move but you literally feel like you are stuck in neutral and can't move. This is because your brain sees whatever you are trying to do as scary or new or unknown and the fear response is activated. This is the moment where you have to work to change things.

When our belief is closer to faith, we act and move and behave in faith. We move as if the thing has already happened. We move as if we're already operating in that way. We move as if we belong there. We move as if we're called there. We move as if we deserve that seat at the table. The closer you move to faith, the stronger your belief is. The closer your identity lines up to the thing you are believing for.

Has there ever been a time where you acted in faith as if that thing had already happened? If so, describe it below:

When there is a disconnect or when there is thought about who you are but your true belief doesn't match it, that's when the friction comes in and there's the rub. That's when your mind says you don't really believe that, so I'm going to keep you in the behaviors and the habits that you do that will keep you feeling tired, stressed, frustrated, anxious, depressed, overwhelmed.

For some people this can show up as imposter syndrome where you doubt your ability or doubt that you are worthy of this vision. This is also why people give up or give in and this is why it feels so hard to change or move away from a way that you have been behaving for years.

As I shared before, we operate mostly from our subconscious brain and it takes energy and time to rewire and reroute our brains to a new mind. It also takes daily, deliberate effort. This is why you need that layered vision to pull you forward when you have thoughts, circumstances or maybe even other people in your life that sow the seed of doubt over this vision.

You're doing this because you have developed an identity that believes where you are because you've been there. You don't have to think about being in this place because it's familiar. Moving out of familiarity takes work, effort and thought. It's a lot easier to stay where you are.

As you were writing the vision, was there a disconnect? A part of you that didn't believe it? Any specific areas that really felt foreign or more uncomfortable than others?

Why do you think there is a disconnect or parts of the vision that didn't ring true for you?

www.soulcarebooks.com

Has there ever been an instance or an area of your life that you have had more faith or belief for others that you have had for yourself? If so, describe it below:

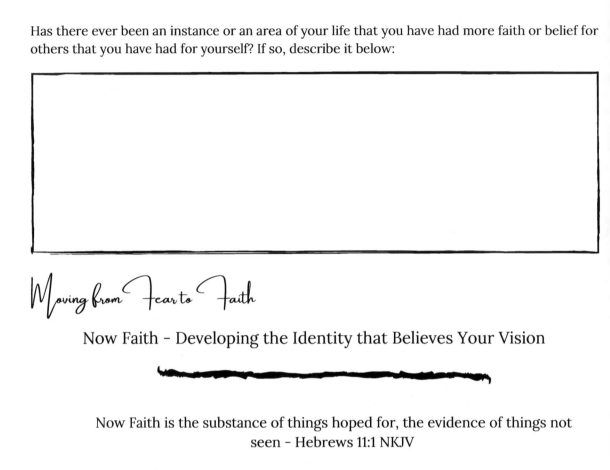

Moving from Fear to Faith

Now Faith - Developing the Identity that Believes Your Vision

Now Faith is the substance of things hoped for, the evidence of things not seen - Hebrews 11:1 NKJV

Developing into the identity that believes your vision will move you from fear to faith. A part of this was creating the visualization in a layered way. The visualization was for you to see the woman that God says that you are and deep down you know who she is to you as well.

We all have room to grow to get to her and so I asked you to think about where she lived, what she looked like, what does she do for a living how does she make decisions, what does she do with her money, if she was living with someone who was she living with what were her surroundings, what did it smell like, what does she eat how does she connect with other people. You did all of that because you were layering the vision, bringing color and substance to it. Almost like a movie in your head. Doing this allowed you to see, hear, smell, taste the entire experience which makes your brain think that it's real.

Right now there may be a gap between where you are and where she is but in between that gap is where the belief comes in. So let's say the vision you saw was your life at a 10, and maybe your life now could be an 8, a 6 or a 5, the difference between the two is where the belief comes in and where the work is. You may not be anywhere near her or you can be very close to her. However, through this, you're creating a belief and having a faith that you can become this woman even at this moment when you may not look anything like her.

When I first worked on the vision in this way, my ideal woman was similar to me, but I wasn't moving in the same way that she was. I wasn't making decisions like her. I wasn't living where she was living. I wasn't acting like she was behaving. I wasn't at peace like she was and so I have been deliberate about moving closer to her and in order to do that I had to RENNEW.

Walk in what God says about you even if your circumstances contradict it.

Thieves of Abundance

We can't just talk about all of the feel good parts about vision and where you want to be. We have to look at those things that can and will get in the way and make a plan for them. Thieves of abundance can cause negative emotions, thoughts and behaviors. These negative thoughts feelings and emotions can store up negative energy and release hormones in your body that support these negative emotions. Cortisol, adrenaline, are released to help you combat whatever has caused that fear or stress response in your body and foster the negative environment.

Answer the questions below and then complete the table below. Read through each thief to abundance and see how you can relate. Doing this will help prepare you and your brain for what inevitably will come - the push back for the return to normal, the status quo, your current identity. Having a plan is half the battle. It gives you a game plan for when you start to use one of these and an opportunity to develop strategies to counteract them.

What external things could present a problem for you while you are creating this life? What steps can you take to address it? (IE: small children, lack of time, family and friends that are used to the way things are)

What internal thoughts and emotions that could present a problem for you while you are creating this life? What steps can you take to address it? (ie:, fear, procrastination, not feeling good enough, not feeling worthy)

What are the top three thoughts that you've believed about yourself that may have been holding you back from your rested, renewed, abundant life?

Now take those three things and name a time when the opposite was true.

Everyone deals with thieves to their abundance. Below, are examples of what these could look like for you. Read each definition and write an example of how you have been impacted next to the ones that you can relate to. There are two extra rows to add thieves to your abundance that were not already in the table below. (Download extra copies of the tables in this chapter at www.soulcarebooks.com

So for each example below there is also a corresponding emotion that goes along with it. Write how your example makes you feel.

Thieves of Abundance

THIEVES OF ABUNDANCE	YOUR EXAMPLE	YOUR FEELING
Fear - fear of the unknown. Fear of failure. Fear of taking next steps. Fear of success. Fear of moving forward. Fear of trying something new.		
Negative Thoughts - thoughts that speak death over you. Thoughts that say, you can't do that. Thoughts that say, what makes you think you're qualified. If said enough they turn into negative loops that play over and over again in your head.		

THIEVES OF ABUNDANCE	YOUR EXAMPLE	YOUR FEELING
Self-doubt- not believing you have what it takes to accomplish a certain goal you've set for yourself. Not believing that you are capable or worthy.		
Imposter Syndrome - believing that you are not worthy. The belief that you don't have what it takes and if someone found out, it would come crumbling down.		
Self-sabotage - taking the fear, doubt, imposter syndrome and acting on them. Not moving, or moving in a way that tears down or takes away from the progress you were trying to make.Trying something new, but as you move forward, you put things in place that will kill it before it starts.		
Procrastination- waiting until the last minute. Putting things off because you are either trying to perfect it or because you have a fear of letting your guard down and show up as yourself.		
Perfectionism - feeling like everything has to be perfect, has to line up perfectly before you can move. Beating yourself up if things aren't just so or if you make mistakes.		

THIEVES OF ABUNDANCE	YOUR EXAMPLE	YOUR FEELING
All or Nothing Thinking- feeling like things have to be a certain way or none of it is any good. Things are always black and white, never any grays. It's either this way or no way at all.		
Being Guarded- keeping a fence around you so others can't hurt you. Not being able to be vulnerable. Cutting others off before they even get a chance to know you		
Jealousy - wishing that you had or were able to do what others are doing. Feeling like what they have or are able to do is better than where you are. Drawing a negative comparison to others. Why not me?		
Gossip- talking about others in a negative way.		
Ruminating - allowing a thought to play over and over again your mind. Creating a negative loop about what could have happened, what should have happened. It impacts your ability to move forward.		

www.soulcarebooks.com

THIEVES OF ABUNDANCE	YOUR EXAMPLE	YOUR FEELING
Unforgiveness- holding onto anger either towards yourself or others. Not being able to let go of issues in your past and they have a hold on you being able to move forward.		
Life Circumstances- things that you may not have any control over. It is just the season of your life where certain life circumstances can be a thief to your abundance.		
Other People – the people in your life who speak negatively to you or don't believe in you. The people who may even be well intentioned, but they have a way of being a thief to your abundance.		

Next we'll discuss tools to feed your faith to counter the thieves of abundance.

Tools to Feed Your Faith

Get ready to stretch! In the tools to feed your faith, you're going to gather tools to help you counter all of those thieves that you just wrote about. Just like the thieves to abundance release hormones, so too does faith. There are corresponding positive emotions and positive impacts on your overall wellbeing that having faith and the corresponding emotions have on your body.

Feelings like joy, peace, gratitude, freedom, love, inspiration, abundance, excitement emit positive hormones like oxytocin.

In order to believe you have to have faith. Faith is something that you have to have because you don't always see the next step. God doesn't always reveal the entire picture to you because if he did, it overwhelm you and keep you from moving forward. Your brain wouldn't be able to handle this all at once. Think about something great or amazing that you've accomplished or experienced. You prayed for it. Now when you initially prayed for this, could you have imagined what it took to get there? If you had imagined what it would have taken to get to that place, what would have been your reaction then? Would you have moved forward? Walked away? Turned in the other direction?

In building your faith, you have to nurture the vision. This is a part of embodying her, really knowing who she is, all of the layering that we talked about and reminding yourself of this on a daily basis. This isn't so that you can live in the future and not in the current moment, but it is so that you can remind yourself of what you're moving toward, so that it is something that is pulling you forward.

There's a book called Knowing your Why by Simon Sinek, but in this instance knowing your why is knowing this woman and knowing the vision of her so that it is strong enough to pull you towards her even in those moments when you don't feel like it. Even in those moments when it requires you to move beyond those behaviors that have been so comfortable for you that they are now habits that you don't have to think about them.

Below you will find several examples of tools you can use to build your belief and build your faith. In the table below, use one of the examples from the Thieves of Abundance table that happened over the last week. Complete the table below with the date and time. Write the situation that occurred. Then check what was your automatic thought or the lie that you have told yourself about that situation. If none of these matches, write your own. Then, on a scale of 1-10, with 1 being the lowest and 10 being the highest, rate the amount of stress this situation caused you. Then check or write what your emotional response was to this.

Combat the Lie

DATE / TIME	SITUATION	AUTOMATIC THOUGHT / LIE YOU TELL YOURSELF	DISTRESS RATING ___ / 10	WHAT'S YOUR EMOTIONAL REACTION
		☐ I will never be good at this ☐ I am a failure ☐ This is too hard ☐ I don't have time for this		☐ I got sad ☐ I gave up ☐ I got angry with myself ☐ I got angry with other people

Now take that same situation and complete the sections below, but add the truth to counter the lie or automatic negative thought. The truth can be a bible verse, an affirmation or past example when the opposite of the lie was true.

www.soulcarebooks.com

Combat the Lie

DATE / TIME	SITUATION	LIE YOU TELL YOURSELF	DISTRESS RATING ___ / 10	TRUTH (BIBLE VERSE, AFFIRMATION, PAST EXAMPLE OF THE OPPOSITE)

Now, take the same situation. Write the situation. Write what you want to change about the situation, then wholly and completely surrender that situation to God. Write what you will surrender to God and why. Then speak out loud what you will surrender. Next, write your intention or commitments around what you are committed to or intend to change about this situation. Finally, write your true feelings about this commitment. (ie: excitement, fear, joy, overwhelm) then surrender your emotions to God.

SITUATION				
WHAT DO YOU WANT TO CHANGE IN THIS SITUATION?				
SURRENDER - WRITE AND SPEAK				
YOUR INTENTION/ COMMITMENT AROUND THIS				
YOUR FEELING AFTER MAKING YOUR COMMITMENT AROUND THIS				
SURRENDER YOUR FEELINGS ABOUT YOUR COMMITMENT TO GOD - WRITE AND SPEAK				

Memorize the Truth

Now transfer just the situation that has caused you distress or has been keeping you stuck and the truth about the situation. After you transfer them, you can take index cards or a mini notepad and write the situation on one side and the truth and how you feel about the truth on the other side. You can also do an audio recording of these so that you can hear them in your own voice as a reminder. This can become your daily motivation or affirmation.

SITUATION	TRUTH (BIBLE VERSE, AFFIRMATION, PAST EXAMPLE OF THE OPPOSITE)	YOUR FEELINGS ABOUT THE SITUATION FRAMED IN TRUTH

Gratitude Rehearsal

Now take these same situations that originally caused you distress and write why you are grateful for the situation in the table below:

You can do the same exercise here and take index cards or a mini notepad and write the situation on one side and why you're grateful on the other. You can also do an audio recording of these so that you can hear them in your own voice as a reminder. Again, these can become your daily motivations or affirmations

SITUATION	GRATITUDE REHEARSAL	YOUR FEELINGS ABOUT THE SITUATION FRAMED IN GRATITUDE

Rehearse the Promise of God

Write it, say it, declare it) until it becomes a part of you. Walk in what God says about you even if your circumstances contradict it. This vision or version of you is what you co-created with God.

Take the vision that you layered in the last chapter and combine it into a paragraph of what you can easily repeat daily. Write it here, speak it out and record it. Record it in either audio or video form. Read it. Repeat it. Listen to it daily for at least the next 67 days to create a new neural pathway in your brain, a new habit, a new belief, a new identity.

Praise and Worship in Advance

Finally, praise God in advance of this version of yourself being true, actually believing that it has already happened. This will train your brain into accepting this version as true to compel you to move forward in obedience towards God's vision/version of you.

Choose the tools here that work best for you. Choose tools that you can use daily as a part of your planner to help you develop the identity and habits of the person who is fully walking in this vision.

Faith takes movement. God is waiting for you to move.

Commitment

1. Meditate on Hebrews 11:1
2. Choose the tools that work best for you and use them daily
3. Work daily to refute old thoughts, behaviors and habits that are trying to keep you stuck
4. Renew your mind daily

Write your commitment here:

Prayer

Ask God to help you in the process of renewing your mind. Ask God to reveal to you the old thought patterns, behaviors and habits that have gotten in your way in the past and give you the courage to push past them. Ask God to help you be consistent in this renewal process and let him know your desire is to be this woman with his help.

Write your prayer below:

www.soulcarebooks.com

The Plan

Chapter 9

Establish Your Blueprint

ESTABLISH YOUR BLUEPRINT

You made it to the end of the guided journal sections of the book. Congratulations! It is definitely a cause for celebration. In this last section of the book, you will establish your blueprint and then walk out that blueprint in the 3 month planner in Chapter 10.

To establish your blueprint, choose your top priority for change from the Soul Care Inventory. As you are establishing your priority for the next 90 days, choose the priority that can impact other areas. You can choose up to three priorities to focus on, but no more than three. It is also helpful to choose areas that compliment each other. For example, if you need to woke on your physical health, you could also incorporate fun/ recreation or the social support because you realize you need to work on improving your friendships.

Don't get anxious in choosing your top priority, use the Soul Care Inventory to help you establish your goals based on the categories that had the lowest scores. Even if you choose one category and realize that another category is one you need to focus on, it's ok to change. As you move forward in your goals, you will begin to feel relief, more days of peace in your chosen area, and feeling less stressed.

"When I dare to be powerful, to use my strength in the service of my vision, then it becomes less and less important whether I am afraid." Audre Lorde

Living a rested, renewed, abundant life is not an accident. It is a series of intentional decisions, feelings, behaviors and habits that form together to create the identity that lines up with the extraordinary. Creating this life requires establishing a rhythm, a momentum to create these habits and eventually creating the identity.

You will establish your blueprint and create your growth over the next 90 days by establishing quarterly, monthly, weekly and daily plans.

In the planner, there are several pieces you will complete. The descriptions for each are below:

Overall Identity, Overall Vision

You've gone through the book to get to this point of understanding and having a clear vision or identity of who you are and how you can live an abundant successful life that feeds your soul. In this area create a concise clear vision of who you are meant to be and keep that vision in mind as you move through the planner.

Quarterly Goal

With the new vision and identity in mind, you will write down your quarterly goals to get there. Many people have said and repeated that it takes 21 days to form a new habit, but the truth is it takes roughly around 60-70 days. It takes this long because in this time frame, you have to give your mind a chance to see the new habit you're trying to form, try to reject it. You will have to be conscious and aware enough to push through to get to the other side of that. The soul care planner is set up to help you do just that.

Quarter in Review

The quarterly review will be done every 90 days to help establish is you are on track to meet your goals. The quarterly review is a way to keep track of your vision and your goals and to ensure that they are alignment with your established vision and goals. There are times when you set a goal or intention and you believe that you are on track until you get to a point in the journey where your progress doesn't line up with where you thought you would be at that moment.

Monthly Goal

The monthly goal, breaks down the quarterly goal down even further to monthly increments. Break down the goal even further so that you can see what is possible in just 30 day increments, documenting and implementing new habits along the way. At the beginning of each month you will write and rewrite your vision. You will set your goals for the month that line up with your overall vision/ identity. You will pray for your month. God's plan for your month and write what you heard from God.

Month in Review

The month in review is similar to the quarterly review. You will use this section to review your monthly goals and to capture what went well for the month and what changes need to be made going into the following month.

Weekly Goal

Break your monthly goals into weekly action plans. At the beginning of each week you will write your vision to help keep you focused. You will write a prayer for your week. Have a sermon note or bible verse to help keep you focused. God's plan for your week. What you heard from God. Your weekly intention. Write and record your affirmations for the week. Create new ones if needed, change them according to your needs for the week.

Week in Review

In the weekly, review, you will write what you are grateful for and write any answered prayers. Each week you will review how your goals are going to help establish your path for the following week.

Daily Goal

Finally you will have daily goals that you will need to accomplish to meet the weekly goal. Each morning, you will pray and write in your planner, rewrite the vision to keep it in the forefront of your mind. Then you will repeat affirmations or bible verses that help to reinforce the vision you have for yourself. You can write these down, memorize them and even record them on your phone in an audio file or a video file. Having a recording to playback helps at times when you have moments of doubt that you can live up to your vision. Next set your daily intentions or goals for the day. At the end of each day, write what you are grateful for and any answered prayers.

My final prayer for you:

My prayer is that in these final pages, you find rest, renewal and abundance. I pray that you discover and feel God's love in every area of your life. I pray that as you move into the woman that God has called you to be that you share your gifts and that God enlarges your territory. I pray that He keeps you from evil and that the love you feel from your relationship with God overflows in abundance and others feel the love emanating from you.

CHAPTER 10

Work Your Blueprint

Quarterly Plan

Q ____

What is your overall 10 vision as described in chapter 7?

What were the three areas from your Soul Care Inventory that caused you the most stress? Which was your #1 issue causing you stress? Write them here with your score and the date.

In the space below, write what you described as a level 10 for each of the three categories above. This will be how you will assess is you are moving closer to your goal.

Month

_____

3 TOP
MONTHLY
INTENTIONS
/GOALS

SUNDAY	MONDAY	TUESDAY

169

20 _____

WEDNESDAY	THURSDAY	FRIDAY	SATURDAY

Month at a Glance ───────────────

Prayer for the Month	God's Plan for My Month

My Overall Vision	Monthly commitment / Intention / Goal

My top 3 Monthly Goals	How will you know you've achieved your monthly goal? (compare to 10 vision for each category)

Week at a Glance

Bible verse for the week	Prayer for the week

God's Plan for My Week	My Overall Vision

Weekly Intentions / Commitments	Weekly Affirmation

Daily Plan _____

My Prayer for Today	My Vision

My Affirmations My Bible Verses	Daily Tasks to complete

My Daily Intentions, Commitments, Goals	Which faith builders did you use to counter the old messages you told yourself today? ie: affirmations, scripture, vision reherasal
○ ○ ○ ○ ○	

Today, I am grateful for / answered prayers:

Daily Plan —————————

My Prayer for Today	My Vision

My Affirmations	My Bible Verses

My Daily Intentions or Goals	Which faith builders did you use to counter the old messages you told yourself today? ie: affirmations, scripture, vision reherasal
○ ○ ○ ○ ○	

Today, I am grateful for / answered prayers:

Daily Plan _____

My Prayer for Today	My Vision

My Affirmations	My Bible Verses

My Daily Intentions or Goals	Which faith builders did you use to counter the old messages you told yourself today? ie: affirmations, scripture, vision rehearsal
○ ○ ○ ○ ○	

Today, I am grateful for / answered prayers:

Daily Plan

My Prayer for Today	My Vision

My Affirmations	My Bible Verses

My Daily Intentions or Goals	Which faith builders did you use to counter the old messages you told yourself today? ie: affirmations, scripture, vision rehearsal
○ ○ ○ ○ ○	

Today, I am grateful for / answered prayers:

www.soulcarebooks.com

Daily Plan _____

My Prayer for Today	My Vision

My Affirmations	My Bible Verses

My Daily Intentions or Goals	Which faith builders did you use to counter the old messages you told yourself today? ie: affirmations, scripture, vision reherasal
○	
○	
○	
○	
○	

Today, I am grateful for / answered prayers:

Daily Plan

My Prayer for Today	My Vision

My Affirmations	My Bible Verses

My Daily Intentions or Goals	Which faith builders did you use to counter the old messages you told yourself today? ie: affirmations, scripture, vision reherasal
○ ○ ○ ○ ○	

Today, I am grateful for / answered prayers:

Daily Plan _____

My Prayer for Today	My Vision

My Affirmations	My Bible Verses

My Daily Intentions or Goals	Which faith builders did you use to counter the old messages you told yourself today? ie: affirmations, scripture, vision reherasal
○	
○	
○	
○	
○	

Today, I am grateful for / answered prayers:

Week in Review

On a scale of 1-10, how well do you think you met your goals this week? circle your answer 1   2   3   4   5   6   7   8   9   10

what went well?	what did you do that worked?

what can you incorporate next week to move you closer to your goal?	what obstacles did you encounter?

what old messages did you tell yourself?	which faith builders did you use to counter the old messages you told yourself? ie: affirmations, scripture, vision rehearsal

www.soulcarebooks.com

This week, I am grateful for / answered prayers:

Week at a Glance

Bible Verse for the week	Prayer for the week

God's Plan for my week	My Overall Vision

Weekly Intent	Weekly Affirmation

Daily Plan _____

My Prayer for Today	My Vision

My Affirmations My Bible Verses	Daily Tasks to complete

My Daily Intentions, Commitments, Goals	Which faith builders did you use to counter the old messages you told yourself today? ie: affirmations, scripture, vision rehearsal
○ ○ ○ ○ ○	

Today, I am grateful for / answered prayers:

Daily Plan _____

My Prayer for Today	My Vision

My Affirmations My Bible Verses	Daily Tasks to complete

My Daily Intentions, commitments, Goals	Which faith builders did you use to counter the old messages you told yourself today? ie: affirmations, scripture, vision reherasal
◯ ◯ ◯ ◯ ◯	

Today, I am grateful for / answered prayers:

Daily Plan _____

My Prayer for Today	My Vision

My Affirmations My Bible Verses	Daily Tasks to complete

My Daily Intentions, Commitments, Goals	Which faith builders did you use to counter the old messages you told yourself today? ie: affirmations, scripture, vision reherasal
○ ○ ○ ○ ○	

Today, I am grateful for / answered prayers:

Daily Plan _____

My Prayer for Today	My Vision

My Affirmations My Bible Verses	Daily Tasks to complete

My Daily Intentions, commitments, Goals	Which faith builders did you use to counter the old messages you told yourself today? ie: affirmations, scripture, vision reherasal
○ ○ ○ ○ ○	

Today, I am grateful for / answered prayers:

Daily Plan _____

My Prayer for Today	My Vision

My Affirmations My Bible Verses	Daily Tasks to complete

My Daily Intentions, Commitments, Goals	which faith builders did you use to counter the old messages you told yourself today? ie: affirmations, scripture, vision reherasal
○ ○ ○ ○ ○	

Today, I am grateful for / answered prayers:

Daily Plan _____

My Prayer for Today	My Vision

My Affirmations My Bible Verses	Daily Tasks to complete

My Daily Intentions, Commitments, Goals	Which faith builders did you use to counter the old messages you told yourself today? ie: affirmations, scripture, vision reherasal
○ ○ ○ ○ ○	

Today, I am grateful for / answered prayers:

Daily Plan _____

My Prayer for Today	My Vision

My Affirmations My Bible Verses	Daily Tasks to complete

My Daily Intentions, Commitments, Goals	which faith builders did you use to counter the old messages you told yourself today? ie: affirmations, scripture, vision reherasal
○ ○ ○ ○ ○	

Today, I am grateful for / answered prayers:

Week in Review _____

On a scale of 1-10, how well do you think you met your goals this week? circle
your answer 1   2   3   4   5   6   7   8   9   10

what went well?	what did you do that worked?

what can you incorporate next week to move you closer to your goal?	what obstacles did you encounter?

what old messages did you tell yourself?	which faith builders did you use to counter the old messages you told yourself? ie: affirmations, scripture, vision rehearsal

This week, I am grateful for / answered prayers:

Week at a Glance

Bible Verse for the week	Prayer for the week

God's Plan for my week	My Overall Vision

Weekly Intent	Weekly Affirmation

Daily Plan _____

My Prayer for Today	My Vision

My Affirmations My Bible Verses	Daily Tasks to complete

My Daily Intentions, Commitments, Goals	Which faith builders did you use to counter the old messages you told yourself today? ie: affirmations, scripture, vision reherasal
○ ○ ○ ○ ○	

Today, I am grateful for / answered prayers:

Daily Plan

My Prayer for Today	My Vision

My Affirmations My Bible Verses	Daily Tasks to complete

My Daily Intentions, Commitments, Goals	Which faith builders did you use to counter the old messages you told yourself today? ie: affirmations, scripture, vision reherasal
○ ○ ○ ○ ○	

Today, I am grateful for / answered prayers:

Daily Plan _____

My Prayer for Today	My Vision

My Affirmations My Bible Verses	Daily Tasks to complete

My Daily Intentions, Commitments, Goals	Which faith builders did you use to counter the old messages you told yourself today? ie: affirmations, scripture, vision reherasal
○ ○ ○ ○ ○	

Today, I am grateful for / answered prayers:

Daily Plan _____

My Prayer for Today	My Vision

My Affirmations My Bible Verses	Daily Tasks to complete

My Daily Intentions, Commitments, Goals	Which faith builders did you use to counter the old messages you told yourself today? ie: affirmations, scripture, vision reherasal
○ ○ ○ ○ ○	

Today, I am grateful for / answered prayers:

Daily Plan _____

My Prayer for Today	My Vision

My Affirmations My Bible Verses	Daily Tasks to complete

My Daily Intentions, Commitments, Goals	Which faith builders did you use to counter the old messages you told yourself today? ie: affirmations, scripture, vision reherasal
○ ○ ○ ○ ○	

Today, I am grateful for / answered prayers:

Daily Plan

My Prayer for Today	My Vision

My Affirmations My Bible Verses	Daily Tasks to complete

My Daily Intentions, Commitments, Goals	which faith builders did you use to counter the old messages you told yourself today? ie: affirmations, scripture, vision reherasal
○	
○	
○	
○	
○	

Today, I am grateful for / answered prayers:

Daily Plan _____

My Prayer for Today	My Vision

My Affirmations My Bible Verses	Daily Tasks to complete

My Daily Intentions, Commitments, Goals	Which faith builders did you use to counter the old messages you told yourself today? ie: affirmations, scripture, vision reherasal
○ ○ ○ ○ ○	

Today, I am grateful for / answered prayers:

Week in Review _____

On a scale of 1-10, how well do you think you met your goals this week? circle
your answer   1   2   3   4   5   6   7   8   9   10

what went well?	what did you do that worked?

what can you incorporate next week to move you closer to your goal?	what obstacles did you encounter?

what old messages did you tell yourself?	Which faith builders did you use to counter the old messages you told yourself? ie: affirmations, scripture, vision rehearsal

This week, I am grateful for / answered prayers:

Week at a Glance ——————

Bible Verse for the week	Prayer for the week

God's Plan for my week	My Overall Vision

Weekly Intent	Weekly Affirmation

Daily Plan _____

My Prayer for Today	My Vision

My Affirmations My Bible Verses	Daily Tasks to complete

My Daily Intentions, Commitments, Goals	Which faith builders did you use to counter the old messages you told yourself today? ie: affirmations, scripture, vision rehearsal
◯ ◯ ◯ ◯ ◯	

Today, I am grateful for / answered prayers:

Daily Plan

My Prayer for Today	My Vision

My Affirmations My Bible Verses	Daily Tasks to complete

My Daily Intentions, Commitments, Goals	which faith builders did you use to counter the old messages you told yourself today? ie: affirmations, scripture, vision reherasal
○ ○ ○ ○ ○	

Today, I am grateful for / answered prayers:

Daily Plan _____

My Prayer for Today	My Vision

My Affirmations My Bible Verses	Daily Tasks to complete

My Daily Intentions, Commitments, Goals	which faith builders did you use to counter the old messages you told yourself today? ie: affirmations, scripture, vision rehearsal
○ ○ ○ ○ ○	

Today, I am grateful for / answered prayers:

Daily Plan

My Prayer for Today	My Vision

My Affirmations My Bible Verses	Daily Tasks to complete

My Daily Intentions, commitments, Goals	which faith builders did you use to counter the old messages you told yourself today? ie: affirmations, scripture, vision reherasal
◯ ◯ ◯ ◯ ◯	

Today, I am grateful for / answered prayers:

Daily Plan _____

My Prayer for Today	My Vision

My Affirmations My Bible Verses	Daily Tasks to complete

My Daily Intentions, Commitments, Goals	which faith builders did you use to counter the old messages you told yourself today? ie: affirmations, scripture, vision rehearsal
○	
○	
○	
○	
○	

Today, I am grateful for / answered prayers:

Daily Plan _____

My Prayer for Today	My Vision

My Affirmations My Bible Verses	Daily Tasks to complete

My Daily Intentions, Commitments, Goals	which faith builders did you use to counter the old messages you told yourself today? ie: affirmations, scripture, vision reherasal
○ ○ ○ ○ ○	

Today, I am grateful for / answered prayers:

Daily Plan _____

My Prayer for Today	My Vision

My Affirmations My Bible Verses	Daily Tasks to complete

My Daily Intentions, Commitments, Goals	Which faith builders did you use to counter the old messages you told yourself today? ie: affirmations, scripture, vision rehearsal
○ ○ ○ ○ ○	

Today, I am grateful for / answered prayers:

Month in Review _____

On a scale of 1-10, how well do you think you met your goals this month? circle your answer 1   2   3   4   5   6   7   8   9   10

what went well?	what did you do that worked?

what can you incorporate next month to move you closer to your goal?	what obstacles did you encounter? what did you notice about the obstacles each week?

which faith builders did you use to counter the old messages?	what are your key take aways for this month?

www.SOULCAREBOOKS.com

This month, I am grateful for / answered prayers:

Month

3 TOP MONTHLY INTENTIONS /GOALS

SUNDAY	MONDAY	TUESDAY

www.soulcarebooks.com

20 _____

WEDNESDAY	THURSDAY	FRIDAY	SATURDAY

Month at a Glance

Prayer for the Month	God's Plan for your Month

My Overall Vision	Monthly commitment / Intention / Goal

My top 3 Monthly Goals	How will you know you've achieved your monthly goal?

Week at a Glance

Bible verse for the week	Prayer for the week

God's Plan for my week	My Overall vision

weekly Intent	weekly Affirmation

Daily Plan _____

My Prayer for Today	My Vision

My Affirmations My Bible Verses	Daily Tasks to complete

My Daily Intentions, Commitments, Goals	which faith builders did you use to counter the old messages you told yourself today? ie: affirmations, scripture, vision reherasal
○ ○ ○ ○ ○	

Today, I am grateful for / answered prayers:

Daily Plan ⎯⎯⎯⎯⎯⎯⎯⎯⎯⎯

My Prayer for Today	My Vision

My Affirmations My Bible Verses	Daily Tasks to complete

My Daily Intentions, Commitments, Goals	which faith builders did you use to counter the old messages you told yourself today? ie: affirmations, scripture, vision rehearsal
○	
○	
○	
○	
○	

Today, I am grateful for / answered prayers:

Daily Plan ─────────

My Prayer for Today	My Vision

My Affirmations My Bible Verses	Daily Tasks to complete

My Daily Intentions, Commitments, Goals	which faith builders did you use to counter the old messages you told yourself today? ie: affirmations, scripture, vision reherasal
○ ○ ○ ○ ○	

Today, I am grateful for / answered prayers:

www.soulcarebooks.com

Daily Plan _____

My Prayer for Today	My Vision

My Affirmations My Bible Verses	Daily Tasks to complete

My Daily Intentions, Commitments, Goals	Which faith builders did you use to counter the old messages you told yourself today? ie: affirmations, scripture, vision reherasal
○ ○ ○ ○ ○	

Today, I am grateful for / answered prayers:

Daily Plan —————————

My Prayer for Today	My Vision

My Affirmations My Bible Verses	Daily Tasks to complete

My Daily Intentions, Commitments, Goals	Which faith builders did you use to counter the old messages you told yourself today? ie: affirmations, scripture, vision reherasal
○ ○ ○ ○ ○	

Today, I am grateful for / answered prayers:

Daily Plan _____

My Prayer for Today	My Vision

My Affirmations My Bible Verses	Daily Tasks to complete

My Daily Intentions, Commitments, Goals	Which faith builders did you use to counter the old messages you told yourself today? ie: affirmations, scripture, vision rehearsal
○ ○ ○ ○ ○	

Today, I am grateful for / answered prayers:

Daily Plan

My Prayer for Today	My Vision

My Affirmations My Bible Verses	Daily Tasks to complete

My Daily Intentions, Commitments, Goals	which faith builders did you use to counter the old messages you told yourself today? ie: affirmations, scripture, vision reherasal
○ ○ ○ ○ ○	

Today, I am grateful for / answered prayers:

Week in Review _____

On a scale of 1-10, how well do you think you met your goals this week? circle
your answer 1   2   3   4   5   6   7   8   9   10

what went well?	what did you do that worked?

what can you incorporate next week to move you closer to your goal?	what obstacles did you encounter?

what old messages did you tell yourself?	Which faith builders did you use to counter the old messages you told yourself? ie: affirmations, scripture, vision reherasal

This week, I am grateful for / answered prayers:

www.soulcarebooks.com

Week at a Glance _____

Bible Verse for the week	Prayer for the week

God's Plan for my week	My Overall Vision

Weekly Intent	Weekly Affirmation

Daily Plan _____

My Prayer for Today	My Vision

My Affirmations My Bible Verses	Daily Tasks to complete

My Daily Intentions, commitments, Goals	Which faith builders did you use to counter the old messages you told yourself today? ie: affirmations, scripture, vision reherasal
◯ ◯ ◯ ◯ ◯	

Today, I am grateful for / answered prayers:

Daily Plan _____

My Prayer for Today	My Vision

My Affirmations My Bible Verses	Daily Tasks to complete

My Daily Intentions, Commitments, Goals	which faith builders did you use to counter the old messages you told yourself today? ie: affirmations, scripture, vision rehearsal
○ ○ ○ ○ ○	

Today, I am grateful for / answered prayers:

Daily Plan _____

My Prayer for Today	My Vision

My Affirmations My Bible Verses	Daily Tasks to complete

My Daily Intentions, Commitments, Goals	Which faith builders did you use to counter the old messages you told yourself today? ie: affirmations, scripture, vision reherasal
○ ○ ○ ○ ○	

Today, I am grateful for / answered prayers:

Daily Plan _____

My Prayer for Today	My Vision

My Affirmations My Bible Verses	Daily Tasks to complete

My Daily Intentions, Commitments, Goals	which faith builders did you use to counter the old messages you told yourself today? ie: affirmations, scripture, vision reherasal
○	
○	
○	
○	
○	

Today, I am grateful for / answered prayers:

Daily Plan _____

My Prayer for Today	My Vision

My Affirmations My Bible Verses	Daily Tasks to complete

My Daily Intentions, Commitments, Goals	which faith builders did you use to counter the old messages you told yourself today? ie: affirmations, scripture, vision reherasal
○ ○ ○ ○ ○	

Today, I am grateful for / answered prayers:

Daily Plan

My Prayer for Today	My Vision

My Affirmations My Bible Verses	Daily Tasks to complete

My Daily Intentions, Commitments, Goals	Which faith builders did you use to counter the old messages you told yourself today? ie: affirmations, scripture, vision rehearsal
○	
○	
○	
○	
○	

Today, I am grateful for / answered prayers:

Daily Plan

My Prayer for Today	My Vision

My Affirmations My Bible Verses	Daily Tasks to complete

My Daily Intentions, Commitments, Goals	which faith builders did you use to counter the old messages you told yourself today? ie: affirmations, scripture, vision reherasal
○ ○ ○ ○ ○	

Today, I am grateful for / answered prayers:

Week in Review _____

On a scale of 1-10, how well do you think you met your goals this week? Circle
your answer   1   2   3   4   5   6   7   8   9   10

what went well?	what did you do that worked?

what can you incorporate next week to move you closer to your goal?	what obstacles did you encounter?

what old messages did you tell yourself?	which faith builders did you use to counter the old messages you told yourself? ie: affirmations, scripture, vision rehearsal

This week, I am grateful for / answered prayers:

Week at a Glance _____

Bible Verse for the Week	Prayer for the Week

God's Plan for my Week	My Overall Vision

Weekly Intent	Weekly Affirmation

Daily Plan

My Prayer for Today	My Vision

My Affirmations My Bible verses	Daily Tasks to complete

My Daily Intentions, Commitments, Goals	which faith builders did you use to counter the old messages you told yourself today? ie: affirmations, scripture, vision reherasal
○ ○ ○ ○ ○	

Today, I am grateful for / answered prayers:

Daily Plan _____

My Prayer for Today	My Vision

My Affirmations My Bible Verses	Daily Tasks to complete

My Daily Intentions, Commitments, Goals	Which faith builders did you use to counter the old messages you told yourself today? ie: affirmations, scripture, vision reherasal
○ ○ ○ ○ ○	

Today, I am grateful for / answered prayers:

Daily Plan

My Prayer for Today	My Vision

My Affirmations My Bible Verses	Daily Tasks to complete

My Daily Intentions, Commitments, Goals	Which faith builders did you use to counter the old messages you told yourself today? ie: affirmations, scripture, vision reherasal
◯ ◯ ◯ ◯ ◯	

Today, I am grateful for / answered prayers:

Daily Plan _____

My Prayer for Today	My Vision

My Affirmations My Bible Verses	Daily Tasks to complete

My Daily Intentions, Commitments, Goals	Which faith builders did you use to counter the old messages you told yourself today? ie: affirmations, scripture, vision rehearsal
○ ○ ○ ○ ○	

Today, I am grateful for / answered prayers:

Daily Plan

My Prayer for Today	My Vision

My Affirmations My Bible Verses	Daily Tasks to complete

My Daily Intentions, Commitments, Goals	which faith builders did you use to counter the old messages you told yourself today? ie: affirmations, scripture, vision reherasal
○ ○ ○ ○ ○	

Today, I am grateful for / answered prayers:

Daily Plan —————————————

My Prayer for Today	My Vision

My Affirmations My Bible Verses	Daily Tasks to complete

My Daily Intentions, Commitments, Goals	Which faith builders did you use to counter the old messages you told yourself today? ie: affirmations, scripture, vision rehearsal
○	
○	
○	
○	
○	

Today, I am grateful for / answered prayers:

Daily Plan

My Prayer for Today	My Vision

My Affirmations My Bible Verses	Daily Tasks to complete

My Daily Intentions, Commitments, Goals	Which faith builders did you use to counter the old messages you told yourself today? ie: affirmations, scripture, vision reherasal
○ ○ ○ ○ ○	

Today, I am grateful for / answered prayers:

Week in Review

On a scale of 1-10, how well do you think you met your goals this week? circle
your answer 1   2   3   4   5   6   7   8   9   10

what went well?	what did you do that worked?

what can you incorporate next week to move you closer to your goal?	what obstacles did you encounter?

what old messages did you tell yourself?	which faith builders did you use to counter the old messages you told yourself? ie: affirmations, scripture, vision rehearsal

www.soulcarebooks.com

This week, I am grateful for / answered prayers:

Week at a Glance

Bible Verse for the week	Prayer for the week

God's Plan for my week	My Overall Vision

Weekly Intent	Weekly Affirmation

Daily Plan ————————————

My Prayer for Today	My Vision

My Affirmations My Bible Verses	Daily Tasks to complete

My Daily Intentions, Commitments, Goals	Which faith builders did you use to counter the old messages you told yourself today? ie: affirmations, scripture, vision reherasal
○ ○ ○ ○ ○	

Today, I am grateful for / answered prayers:

Daily Plan _____

My Prayer for Today	My Vision

My Affirmations My Bible Verses	Daily Tasks to complete

My Daily Intentions, Commitments, Goals	Which faith builders did you use to counter the old messages you told yourself today? ie: affirmations, scripture, vision reherasal
○	
○	
○	
○	
○	

Today, I am grateful for / answered prayers:

Daily Plan

My Prayer for Today	My Vision

My Affirmations My Bible Verses	Daily Tasks to complete

My Daily Intentions, Commitments, Goals	Which faith builders did you use to counter the old messages you told yourself today? ie: affirmations, scripture, vision reherasal
○ ○ ○ ○ ○	

Today, I am grateful for / answered prayers:

Daily Plan

My Prayer for Today	My Vision

My Affirmations My Bible Verses	Daily Tasks to complete

My Daily Intentions, Commitments, Goals	Which faith builders did you use to counter the old messages you told yourself today? ie: affirmations, scripture, vision reherasal
○ ○ ○ ○ ○	

Today, I am grateful for / answered prayers:

Daily Plan ──────────

My Prayer for Today	My Vision

My Affirmations My Bible Verses	Daily Tasks to complete

My Daily Intentions, Commitments, Goals	Which faith builders did you use to counter the old messages you told yourself today? ie: affirmations, scripture, vision reherasal
○ ○ ○ ○ ○	

Today, I am grateful for / answered prayers:

Daily Plan ———————————

My Prayer for Today	My Vision

My Affirmations My Bible Verses	Daily Tasks to complete

My Daily Intentions, Commitments, Goals	Which faith builders did you use to counter the old messages you told yourself today? ie: affirmations, scripture, vision rehearsal
○ ○ ○ ○ ○	

Today, I am grateful for / answered prayers:

Daily Plan

My Prayer for Today	My Vision

My Affirmations My Bible Verses	Daily Tasks to complete

My Daily Intentions, Commitments, Goals	Which faith builders did you use to counter the old messages you told yourself today? ie: affirmations, scripture, vision reherasal
○ ○ ○ ○ ○	

Today, I am grateful for / answered prayers:

Month in Review _____

On a scale of 1-10, how well do you think you met your goals this month? circle
your answer 1   2   3   4   5   6   7   8   9   10

what went well?	what did you do that worked?

what can you incorporate next month to move you closer to your goal?	what obstacles did you encounter? what did you notice about the obstacles each week?

which faith builders did you use to counter the old messages?	what are your key take aways for this month?

www.SOULCAREBOOKS.com

This month, I am grateful for / answered prayers:

Month

SUNDAY

MONDAY

TUESDAY

3 TOP MONTHLY INTENTIONS /GOALS

20 _____

WEDNESDAY	THURSDAY	FRIDAY	SATURDAY

255   www.soulcarebooks.com

Month at a Glance ————————

Prayer for the Month	God's Plan for My Month

My Overall Vision	Monthly Commitment / Intention / Goal

My top 3 Monthly Goals	How will you know you've achieved your monthly goal? (compare to 10 vision for each category)

Week at a Glance

Bible Verse for the week	Prayer for the week

God's Plan for My week	My Overall Vision

weekly Intentions / Commitments	weekly Affirmation

Daily Plan _____

My Prayer for Today	My Vision

My Affirmations My Bible Verses	Daily Tasks to complete

My Daily Intentions, Commitments, Goals	Which faith builders did you use to counter the old messages you told yourself today? ie: affirmations, scripture, vision reherasal
○ ○ ○ ○ ○	

Today, I am grateful for / answered prayers:

Daily Plan _____

My Prayer for Today	My Vision

My Affirmations My Bible Verses	Daily Tasks to complete

My Daily Intentions, Commitments, Goals	Which faith builders did you use to counter the old messages you told yourself today? ie: affirmations, scripture, vision reherasal
○ ○ ○ ○ ○	

Today, I am grateful for / answered prayers:

Daily Plan _____

My Prayer for Today	My Vision

My Affirmations My Bible Verses	Daily Tasks to complete

My Daily Intentions, Commitments, Goals	Which faith builders did you use to counter the old messages you told yourself today? ie: affirmations, scripture, vision reherasal
○ ○ ○ ○ ○	

Today, I am grateful for / answered prayers:

Daily Plan _____

My Prayer for Today	My Vision

My Affirmations My Bible Verses	Daily Tasks to complete

My Daily Intentions, commitments, Goals	which faith builders did you use to counter the old messages you told yourself today? ie: affirmations, scripture, vision rehearsal
○ ○ ○ ○ ○	

Today, I am grateful for / answered prayers:

Daily Plan _____

My Prayer for Today	My Vision

My Affirmations My Bible Verses	Daily Tasks to Complete

My Daily Intentions, Commitments, Goals	Which faith builders did you use to counter the old messages you told yourself today? ie: affirmations, scripture, vision rehearsal
○ ○ ○ ○ ○	

Today, I am grateful for / answered prayers:

Daily Plan ───────────────

My Prayer for Today	My Vision

My Affirmations My Bible Verses	Daily Tasks to complete

My Daily Intentions, Commitments, Goals	Which faith builders did you use to counter the old messages you told yourself today? ie: affirmations, scripture, vision rehearsal
○ ○ ○ ○ ○	

Today, I am grateful for / answered prayers:

Daily Plan _____

My Prayer for Today	My Vision

My Affirmations My Bible Verses	Daily Tasks to complete

My Daily Intentions, Commitments, Goals	Which faith builders did you use to counter the old messages you told yourself today? ie: affirmations, scripture, vision reherasal
○ ○ ○ ○ ○	

Today, I am grateful for / answered prayers:

Week in Review _____

On a scale of 1-10, how well do you think you met your goals this week? circle
your answer 1   2   3   4   5   6   7   8   9   10

what went well?	what did you do that worked?

what can you incorporate next week to move you closer to your goal?	what obstacles did you encounter?

what old messages did you tell yourself?	which faith builders did you use to counter the old messages you told yourself? ie: affirmations, scripture, vision reherasal

This week, I am grateful for / answered prayers:

Week at a Glance

Bible Verse for the week	Prayer for the week

God's Plan for my week	My Overall Vision

Weekly Intent	Weekly Affirmation

Daily Plan _____

My Prayer for Today	My Vision

My Affirmations My Bible Verses	Daily Tasks to complete

My Daily Intentions, Commitments, Goals	which faith builders did you use to counter the old messages you told yourself today? ie: affirmations, scripture, vision reherasal
○ ○ ○ ○ ○	

Today, I am grateful for / answered prayers:

Daily Plan ───────────

My Prayer for Today	My Vision

My Affirmations My Bible Verses	Daily Tasks to complete

My Daily Intentions, Commitments, Goals	Which faith builders did you use to counter the old messages you told yourself today? ie: affirmations, scripture, vision reherasal
○ ○ ○ ○ ○	

Today, I am grateful for / answered prayers:

Daily Plan _____

My Prayer for Today	My Vision

My Affirmations My Bible Verses	Daily Tasks to complete

My Daily Intentions, commitments, Goals	Which faith builders did you use to counter the old messages you told yourself today? ie: affirmations, scripture, vision reherasal
○ ○ ○ ○ ○	

Today, I am grateful for / answered prayers:

Daily Plan ─────────

My Prayer for Today	My Vision

My Affirmations My Bible Verses	Daily Tasks to Complete

My Daily Intentions, Commitments, Goals	Which faith builders did you use to counter the old messages you told yourself today? ie: affirmations, scripture, vision reherasal
○ ○ ○ ○ ○	

Today, I am grateful for / answered prayers:

Daily Plan _____

My Prayer for Today	My Vision

My Affirmations My Bible Verses	Daily Tasks to complete

My Daily Intentions, Commitments, Goals	which faith builders did you use to counter the old messages you told yourself today? ie: affirmations, scripture, vision reherasal
○ ○ ○ ○ ○	

Today, I am grateful for / answered prayers:

Daily Plan _____

My Prayer for Today	My Vision

My Affirmations My Bible verses	Daily Tasks to complete

My Daily Intentions, Commitments, Goals	Which faith builders did you use to counter the old messages you told yourself today? ie: affirmations, scripture, vision reherasal
○ ○ ○ ○ ○	

Today, I am grateful for / answered prayers:

Daily Plan _____

My Prayer for Today	My Vision

My Affirmations My Bible Verses	Daily Tasks to complete

My Daily Intentions, Commitments, Goals	Which faith builders did you use to counter the old messages you told yourself today? ie: affirmations, scripture, vision reherasal
○ ○ ○ ○ ○	

Today, I am grateful for / answered prayers:

Week in Review _____

On a scale of 1-10, how well do you think you met your goals this week? Circle your answer   1   2   3   4   5   6   7   8   9   10

What went well?	What did you do that worked?

What can you incorporate next week to move you closer to your goal?	What obstacles did you encounter?

What old messages did you tell yourself?	Which faith builders did you use to counter the old messages you told yourself? ie: affirmations, scripture, vision reherasal

This week, I am grateful for / answered prayers:

Week at a Glance

Bible Verse for the week	Prayer for the week

God's Plan for my week	My Overall Vision

Weekly Intent	Weekly Affirmation

Daily Plan _____

My Prayer for Today	My Vision

My Affirmations My Bible Verses	Daily Tasks to complete

My Daily Intentions, Commitments, Goals	Which faith builders did you use to counter the old messages you told yourself today? ie: affirmations, scripture, vision reherasal
○ ○ ○ ○ ○	

Today, I am grateful for / answered prayers:

Daily Plan ⎯⎯⎯⎯⎯⎯⎯⎯⎯⎯

My Prayer for Today	My Vision

My Affirmations My Bible Verses	Daily Tasks to complete

My Daily Intentions, Commitments, Goals	Which faith builders did you use to counter the old messages you told yourself today? ie: affirmations, scripture, vision reherasal
○ ○ ○ ○ ○	

Today, I am grateful for / answered prayers:

Daily Plan _____

My Prayer for Today	My Vision

My Affirmations My Bible verses	Daily Tasks to complete

My Daily Intentions, Commitments, Goals	Which faith builders did you use to counter the old messages you told yourself today? ie: affirmations, scripture, vision rehearsal
○ ○ ○ ○ ○	

Today, I am grateful for / answered prayers:

Daily Plan _____

My Prayer for Today	My Vision

My Affirmations My Bible Verses	Daily Tasks to Complete

My Daily Intentions, Commitments, Goals	Which faith builders did you use to counter the old messages you told yourself today? ie: affirmations, scripture, vision reherasal
○ ○ ○ ○ ○	

Today, I am grateful for / answered prayers:

Daily Plan _____

My Prayer for Today	My Vision

My Affirmations My Bible Verses	Daily Tasks to complete

My Daily Intentions, Commitments, Goals	Which faith builders did you use to counter the old messages you told yourself today? ie: affirmations, scripture, vision reherasal
○ ○ ○ ○ ○	

Today, I am grateful for / answered prayers:

Daily Plan _____

My Prayer for Today	My Vision

My Affirmations My Bible Verses	Daily Tasks to complete

My Daily Intentions, commitments, Goals	Which faith builders did you use to counter the old messages you told yourself today? ie: affirmations, scripture, vision reherasal
◯	
◯	
◯	
◯	
◯	

Today, I am grateful for / answered prayers:

Daily Plan _____

My Prayer for Today	My Vision

My Affirmations My Bible Verses	Daily Tasks to complete

My Daily Intentions, Commitments, Goals	Which faith builders did you use to counter the old messages you told yourself today? ie: affirmations, scripture, vision reheransal
○ ○ ○ ○ ○	

Today, I am grateful for / answered prayers:

Week in Review _____

On a scale of 1-10, how well do you think you met your goals this week? circle
your answer 1   2   3   4   5   6   7   8   9   10

what went well?	what did you do that worked?

what can you incorporate next week to move you closer to your goal?	what obstacles did you encounter?

what old messages did you tell yourself?	which faith builders did you use to counter the old messages you told yourself? ie: affirmations, scripture, vision reherasal

www.soulcarebooks.com

This week, I am grateful for / answered prayers:

Week at a Glance

Bible Verse for the week	Prayer for the week

God's Plan for my week	My Overall vision

weekly Intent	weekly Affirmation

Daily Plan _____

My Prayer for Today	My Vision

My Affirmations My Bible verses	Daily Tasks to complete

My Daily Intentions, Commitments, Goals	which faith builders did you use to counter the old messages you told yourself today? ie: affirmations, scripture, vision reherasal
○	
○	
○	
○	
○	

Today, I am grateful for / answered prayers:

Daily Plan ─────────────────

My Prayer for Today	My Vision

My Affirmations My Bible verses	Daily Tasks to complete

My Daily Intentions, commitments, Goals	which faith builders did you use to counter the old messages you told yourself today? ie: affirmations, scripture, vision rehearsal
◯ ◯ ◯ ◯ ◯	

Today, I am grateful for / answered prayers:

Daily Plan _____

My Prayer for Today	My Vision

My Affirmations My Bible Verses	Daily Tasks to complete

My Daily Intentions, Commitments, Goals	Which faith builders did you use to counter the old messages you told yourself today? ie: affirmations, scripture, vision reherasal
○ ○ ○ ○ ○	

Today, I am grateful for / answered prayers:

Daily Plan

My Prayer for Today	My Vision

My Affirmations My Bible Verses	Daily Tasks to complete

My Daily Intentions, Commitments, Goals	which faith builders did you use to counter the old messages you told yourself today? ie: affirmations, scripture, vision rehearsal
○ ○ ○ ○ ○	

Today, I am grateful for / answered prayers:

Daily Plan _____

My Prayer for Today	My Vision

My Affirmations My Bible Verses	Daily Tasks to complete

My Daily Intentions, Commitments, Goals	which faith builders did you use to counter the old messages you told yourself today? ie: affirmations, scripture, vision reherasal
○ ○ ○ ○ ○	

Today, I am grateful for / answered prayers:

Daily Plan

My Prayer for Today	My Vision

My Affirmations My Bible Verses	Daily Tasks to complete

My Daily Intentions, Commitments, Goals	Which faith builders did you use to counter the old messages you told yourself today? ie: affirmations, scripture, vision reherasal
○ ○ ○ ○ ○	

Today, I am grateful for / answered prayers:

Daily Plan _____

My Prayer for Today	My Vision

My Affirmations My Bible Verses	Daily Tasks to complete

My Daily Intentions, Commitments, Goals	which faith builders did you use to counter the old messages you told yourself today? ie: affirmations, scripture, vision reherasal
○ ○ ○ ○ ○	

Today, I am grateful for / answered prayers:

Month in Review _____

On a scale of 1-10, how well do you think you met your goals this month? circle
your answer 1   2   3   4   5   6   7   8   9   10

what went well?	what did you do that worked?

what can you incorporate next month to move you closer to your goal?	what obstacles did you encounter? what did you notice about the obstacles each week?

which faith builders did you use to counter the old messages?	what are your key take aways for this month?

This month, I am grateful for / answered prayers:

www.soulcarebooks.com

Quarterly Review

Q _____

On a scale of 1-10, how well do you think you met your goals this quarter? circle your answer

1   2   3   4   5   6   7   8   9   10

Write the three primary goals you worked on this quarter, rate and date them. Then compare your scores from the beginning of the quarter.

what went well?	what obstacles did you encounter?
what are your key takeaways for this quarter?	**How will you build on these goals in the next quarter?**

This quarter, I am grateful for / answered prayers:

Made in the USA
Las Vegas, NV
22 November 2023

81344689R00164